Life in a Drop of Water

Life in a Drop of Water

GEORGE I. SCHWARTZ

PUBLISHED FOR THE AMERICAN MUSEUM OF NATURAL HISTORY

The Natural History Press, Garden City, New York

The Natural History Press, publisher for The American
Museum of Natural History, is a division of Doubleday
& Company, Inc. Directed by a joint editorial board made
up of members of the staff of both the Museum and
Doubleday, The Natural History Press publishes books
and periodicals in all branches of the life and earth sci-
ences, including anthropology and astronomy. The Natural
History Press has its editorial offices at The American
Museum of Natural History, Central Park West at 79th
Street, New York, New York 10024, and its business
offices at 501 Franklin Avenue, Garden City, New York
11530.

TO MY WIFE BERNICE
Companion in the search

PREFACE

The writing of this book was a long but delightful experience. Every aspect of its production was fun. The many trips to pond, swamp, ocean, and bay were always full of surprises—and occasionally brought disappointments as well. Mastering the use of the microscope provided its rewards. Solving the problems of photographing the vibrant microscopic life of the waters was an unending challenge. Too often the big ones got away, unphotographed. They will be seen again, and finally photographed, since I intend to continue the search.

A word about the title of the book is in order here. *Life in a Drop of Water* is not an original title. It so completely represented the story I wished to tell that I insisted on using it. I recognize that it might be misleading; but when the "drop of water" is recognized to be representative of thousands of drops, each different and yet the same, then it stands out as the only title that fits the story I sought to tell. It was good to learn that here, too, Antony van Leeuwenhoek first used the expression in a slightly different way when he said, ". . . no more pleasant sight has come before my eye than these many thousands of living creatures, seen all alive in a drop of water . . ."

My debts to many individuals are numerous. I alone am responsible for its shortcomings and errors. I present it to you, the reader, in the hope that it may bring you some measure of the wonder and excitement which have been mine in its preparation.

G.I.S.

CONTENTS

Life in a Drop of Water

INTRODUCTION

The world of living things is a world of endless fascination and excitement. Men have observed this world more or less accurately for tens of thousands of years—or perhaps even longer. In the early days, they were most successful in learning about plants and animals when these were useful to man or were likely to bring him harm.

In more recent times, during the last four or five hundred years, explorers began to expand the known world. Expeditions were sent to all parts of the earth to chart the waters for navigation. Some searched for new lands. Many of them were also commissioned to collect plants and animals and to bring them back for detailed study. Often a ship's naturalist was brought along to provide skill in collecting and preserving the specimens. He also identified some of the collected organisms.

The explorations revealed an impressive variety of living things which populate both land and waters from pole to pole. Many were being seen for the first time. New types of plants and animals were being discovered almost daily. The result is that today the number of kinds of plants and animals known to be alive on the earth totals well over a million and continues to grow.

One part of this world of living things, though, was unknown and unsuspected up to about three hundred years ago. This was the world of microscopic life; a world whose inhabitants are so small

Portrait of Antony van Leeuwenhoek painted in 1688 when he was fifty-six years old. The portrait was painted by Johannes Verkolje, also a citizen of Delft, the city where Leeuwenhoek was born and lived most of his long life. (*Fotocommissie, Rijksmuseum, Amsterdam, Holland*)

that we need devices which enlarge them so that they can be seen clearly. These optical devices (lenses) were a long time in coming. The first microscopes were built and used early in the seventeenth century. The microscope is truly a modern invention.

It was not long after this that Antony van Leeuwenhoek found and described the wonderful world of microscopic life. He did this with lenses he ground and mounted as simple microscopes. He made more than 250 in his lifetime and used them for more than fifty years with great skill and unusual accuracy.

For as long as I can remember, roaming through fields and woods and along the ocean shore held special delights. The search for

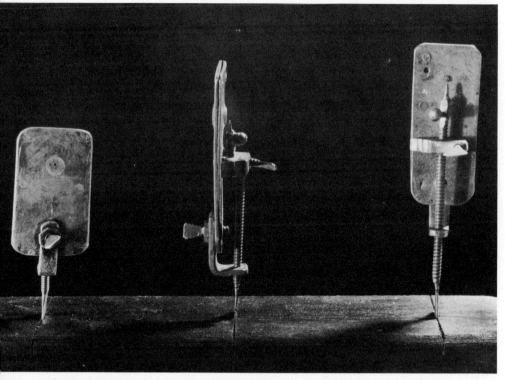

Three of Leeuwenhoek's microscopes. The one on the left is mounted in silver and was able to magnify about 80 ×. The other two are made of brass. The center microscope has no lens. The one on the right magnified about 125 ×. The two brass microscopes are about 6 centimeters long (2¾ inches). (*National Museum for the History of Science, Leiden, Holland*)

plants and animals was usually rewarded by finding a new one—at least new to me. This is the special kind of discovery always open to the young. Any body of water—fresh or salt—with its many living inhabitants had a particular attraction. I never lost my sense of wonder for the living things of water. I waited anxiously for the arrival of each spring. It meant frog and salamander eggs followed by the succession of swimming, crawling, and gliding insects. Some took to the air as they completed the water stages of their complex lives.

My first look through a microscope opened up a whole new world. There was a drop of pond water on the slide. Such strange creatures hurried and scurried by. Not one was familiar. And there were so many in a single drop.

I shared this experience with many others because there was only one microscope for a large number of us. I had but a minute as my share of looking time. A minute of viewing was enough to make it clear that someday I must have my own microscope. It did not matter how long I had to wait. The wait was really a long one.

After several years had passed, I learned that a physician friend wanted to sell his microscope. He knew how much I wanted a good microscope of my own and made the price one I could reach. Later I found that it was worth a good deal more than he asked me to pay for it. He said he wanted to know that it was in good hands.

Buying my own microscope was the beginning of over forty-five years of intensive, exciting, and rewarding viewing. Now the waters really called out to me. Every pond, brook, swamp, and marsh within reach was visited. Each gave up a jar or two of its water, often with the addition of some bottom mud or a few water plants. Then the jars were taken home to search and explore the water one drop at a time.

Many drops were disappointing. It is not always easy to pick up a single drop of water with enough organisms to be located easily. But I found that many microscopic living things look, to the unaided eye, like tiny specks scattered through the jar in which they are collected. A magnifying glass or hand lens helped to locate them and ensured getting a few on the slide for examination. Before long it was fairly easy to prepare slide after slide with some life in each drop of water.

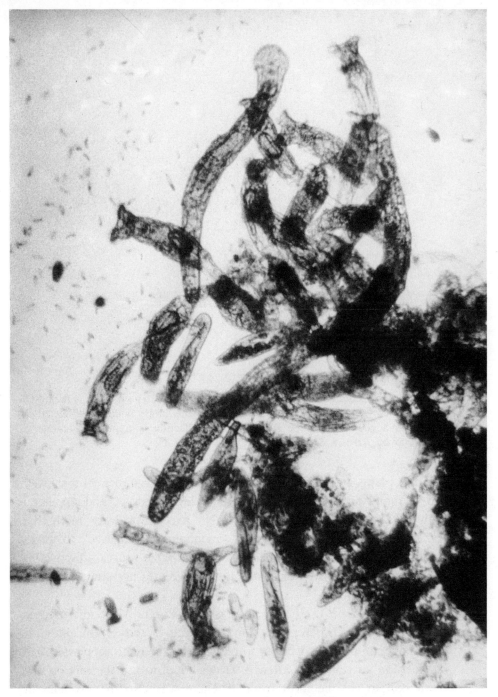

A drop of fresh water magnified about 50 ×. There are hundreds of living things, including some large relatives of the earthworm; some rotifers; and three kinds of protozoa, including a number of paramecia. The dark areas consist largely of decaying plant material. This is quite a busy place.

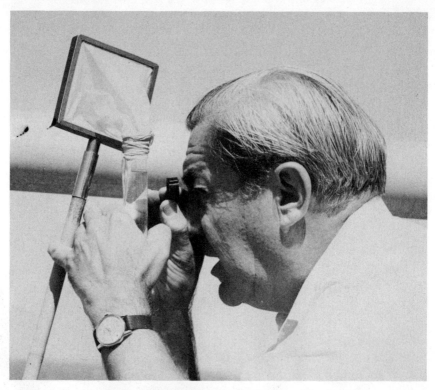

Examining a container with many marine organisms. The hand lens magnifies 10 ✕—enough to recognize some of the larger animals collected. This is a good way to be sure that the collection is a productive one. (*Photo by Bernice Schwartz*)

Some plants and animals were present in large numbers and showed up in many drops. Others were much less common and appeared only rarely. This was a challenge. No two drops were really the same. The kinds of living things I saw changed from week to week, even when the water was collected from the same source. Discoveries were easy to come by. For a long time nature did not seem to repeat herself.

The microscope itself was not easy to master. Most microscopic life is almost transparent. If the light used is too bright, little, if anything, can be seen. I began to realize why the microscope is called a precision instrument. I knew it was essential to use the microscope with skill to get the most from it. There was also the problem of collecting more plants and animals in each jar of water.

The floating, drifting microscopic plants and animals which are found in the surface waters of ocean and pond are known as plankton. Special nets are available for concentrating and collecting these living things. They are given the obvious name of plankton nets. There are many kinds, depending on how they will be used, but they are basically the same. They consist of a cone-shaped net of finely woven cloth at the narrow end of which is a collecting bottle or tube. The number of threads per inch in the cloth will determine how fine the openings are and how small the animals and plants collected will be. When larger organisms are sought, the weave is a coarse one and the smaller plants and animals will pass through the openings.

As a plankton net is drawn through the water, the organisms large enough to be caught by it are concentrated in the bottle or tube, while the excess water passes through the fine openings in the

Here is a fresh-water plankton net in use. I am looking at a rich haul of *Daphnia,* the water flea. I have a second net that uses the same handle, which I use exclusively for marine collecting.

cloth. The living things in many gallons of water are collected in the small container. My own nets are made of a fine nylon cloth woven with 250 threads to the inch. The same cloth is used in flour mills to sift flour and is known as bolting cloth. I use two nets; one for fresh-water organisms, the other for those living in salt water.

There was no longer a problem in getting things to look at. After a period of examining the life of the ponds, lakes, marshes, and swamps, I felt the need to explore the waters of the Atlantic Ocean. It soon became clear that marine life was much richer with living things than any kind of fresh water. I was not interested in accumulating a number of organisms as a kind of conquest. I was interested in each as a living thing which had some measure of success as a living thing. What kind of living thing was it? How was it equipped to survive? I could answer some of my questions by observation. Others demanded more information than observation alone could provide. This meant using references to identify the organisms seen and to learn more about them, their life histories, and their ways of life.

There were many reference books, but it was not always possible to find the information wanted. Specialists could be consulted but the demands on their time and energy are not always reasonable when a more careful search is needed. Finding the answers always brought a sense of achievement. But there must always remain many unanswered questions.

I wanted to have some record of many of the objects I collected and studied. One way of doing this was to draw them and to make extensive notes. But it requires more skill and talent than I have to do this well. I decided to use photography to accomplish the same results. This is not as easy as it sounds. Photography through a microscope is a special art and requires many years of painful effort and mistakes to begin to achieve some success.

Most of the bodies of water from which I have collected microorganisms are located in New York City or very close to it. Many collecting sites which I once favored have long since disappeared. Ponds and swamps have been filled in and replaced by homes and shopping centers. Somehow, it was always possible to find small bodies of water to replace those no longer available. The shore of the Atlantic Ocean was even easier to reach and to use as a never-ending source of microscopic life. It is not necessary to travel to far-off places to explore "life in a drop of water."

Actually this is the story of many drops of water, from many places. It is illustrated with many photographs I made in recording my own adventures. It is intended to be an introduction to the life it pictures. It is also an invitation to you to explore this world on your own. Good microscopes are much easier to obtain than they once were. They are not too expensive if you consider the delight and enjoyment they will bring in many years of use.

Chapter 1

EXPLORING THE WORLD OF MICROSCOPIC LIFE

You and I are alive. A rock is not alive. That's easy, isn't it? Anyone can see that we are alive and that rocks are not alive. But what about all the other kinds of things on the earth? Which are alive and which are not? You might even challenge me and ask: "How do you know that you and I are alive? Prove that we are alive."

Let's try. This morning you were hungry when you got up. You ate your breakfast. You took in enough food to give your body the energy it needed to keep you going at your work and at play. All living things need energy for the things they do, and they get their energy from the food they take in, by burning it. This releases the energy locked up in the molecules of food.

What do living things do with this energy? You and I move. We walk or we run; we use our arms and hands to lift things. That is movement. Movement requires energy.

A fish swims and we realize that it, too, is alive. A butterfly moves from flower to flower and we agree that it is alive. And so is the beetle crawling over the leaves of a milkweed.

A stone rolls down a hill. A leaf flutters to the ground when detached from a tree. But these are different kinds of movement. The stone and leaf do not move by their own power. They are moved by the wind and by the gravitational pull of the earth. The energy that moves them comes from the outside. We have a clue that they are not alive.

I am told that I weighed about 7 pounds when I was born. I weigh 160 pounds now. Quite a bit more of "me" has been produced. Food was needed to produce the new material in my body. The same thing happened to you. Your body was also very small when you were born. Since then a lot more of "you" has been formed, because you, too, have been taking in food. You used some of the food to provide energy for your movement. Some of the energy was needed just to keep you alive. Some of the food was the raw material which your body used to grow—that is, to make more of you. To do this the body also needed energy to put together the chemical building blocks from the food to form the more complex molecules of "you."

You and I react to many things in our environment. We respond to sound and light as well as to touch and taste and pain. When I touch something hot I quickly pull my hand back. I have reacted or responded. You may be about to cross a busy street when the sound of an automobile horn causes you to stop suddenly. You have reacted. You notice a cat suddenly confronted by a strange dog. It reacts in the ways in which cats have behaved toward dogs for hundreds of years.

All living things react, even the most simple ones. They do not all react in the same way, but they are affected by the same kinds of forces or conditions: light, touch, chemicals, sound, gravity, and the other factors which also cause us to behave. Most of the reactions of simple living things are very simple. They move away from something or they move toward it. Not much more is evident. But they must have been successful in avoiding the possible dangers around them because they are still around and in large numbers.

There is more to being alive than moving and growing and reacting. If any object shows all three of these abilities we are fairly sure that it is alive. We also decide that it has other abilities as well.

Perhaps your dog has just had a litter of puppies or the family cat has just given birth to a litter of kittens. You have long been aware of birth and you know that living things produce new individuals very much like themselves. They reproduce their own kind. This is true of the simplest living things on earth as it is of the most complex ones.

You and I weren't always here. Before we were born, our parents were here, and before them, their parents were on the earth. Living things have been present on the earth in an unending chain which reaches back billions of years. It is evident that no one living thing could possibly live that long. Since living things have the ability to reproduce, they continue to live as types, and to remain on the earth.

The individual living thing dies and disappears, yet its kind survives. Many thousands of types of living things have also disappeared from the earth completely. These types, for one reason or another, were unable to adapt to the changing conditions. Others were unable to produce enough new individuals to keep the race going. This happened to all the dinosaurs as well as to the four-toed horse. It also happened to countless other animals and plants as well. It is happening now and will continue to occur in the future. But life will continue, in the form of organisms which are adapted to survive and which can reproduce their kind.

Life is found and thrives in a wide range of environments. Some kinds of living things live on mountains, while others exist in deserts; some find the conditions in caves ideal for them, while others make the ocean floor their home; a tropical jungle and the arctic seas are favored by their own populations of living things. Most living things need special conditions that are not found all over the earth. The hookworm lives in the intestine of man; the sidewinder rattlesnake is found in dry, desertlike areas of the western United States; the animal which causes malaria in man spends part of its life in the bodies of two animals—man and the *Anopheles* mosquito.

The kinds of plants and animals alive on the earth today are the products of thousands or even millions of years of change. Those animals which could adjust to their changing environments survived; the ones which could not, disappeared.

Being alive, then, means the ability to take in food and to use that food for energy; to grow, to move; to behave; and to reproduce other individuals like itself. But this isn't the whole story. Among the simpler living things are creatures which present problems. They do not exactly fit the criteria we have suggested. Many biologists are not satisfied with any definitions of life. They prefer to accept the fact that many creatures are obviously alive and to spend their time observing and studying and experimenting with them. Why worry about these difficulties? They do not keep us from observing and enjoying all kinds of living creatures.

The plants and animals we know best can easily be seen by the naked eye. But there is a world of life too small to be seen without stronger lenses than those in our own eyes. If we could make ourselves small enough to enter a drop of water to explore it, we would find it a dangerous and perilous world indeed. We can see this world safely by using a microscope. It puts us deep in this world, just as a space capsule could take us into the vast world of space.

You do not need an expensive microscope to make this journey. The microscopes which so many young people own will perform very well. Through them you will be able to see many of the kinds of living things which are found in such large numbers all over the world. The fresh-water animals and plants described and pictured here are common, plentiful, and easy to find in all parts of the United States. The marine types can be collected from the ocean or bays, gulfs, and other bodies of salt water connected with oceans.

A lens is a piece of glass curved on one or both surfaces. The best ones are carefully ground of special glass sometimes to an accuracy of one-millionth of an inch. The amount of curvature of a lens determines the magnifying or enlarging power of the lens. If you do not have a microscope, an inexpensive hand lens that magnifies objects 10 or 15 times is a good way to start your observations. It will reveal some details of structure as well as the active swimming movements of the remarkable little creatures you can find.

A hand lens is really a simple microscope. A compound microscope consists of two sets of lenses, one at each end of a metal tube or barrel. It makes possible much higher magnification than does a simple one. The lenses near the object being examined form an image of the object. The second set of lenses enlarges the image thus formed. If each set of lenses magnifies 10 times, the total magnification is then 100 times; that is, 10×10. A good compound microscope can provide magnifications of 1000 times or more with the right combination of lenses.

To examine the world of the very small with a compound microscope, you place a drop of pond water on a 3-inch by 1-inch piece of glass called a microscope slide and cover it with a thin piece of cover glass. The cover glass protects the drop and prevents the

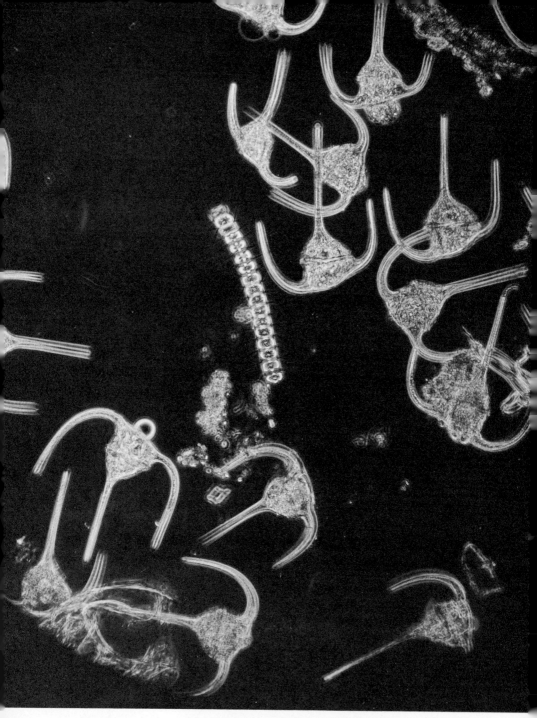

A drop of salt water magnified about 85 ×. The creature with three prongs is *Ceratium,* a dinoflagellate. This water was collected in the late spring when *Ceratium* was multiplying rapidly. The interesting-looking organism in the middle of the photograph is a diatom, the most important plant type in the ocean.

water from evaporating too fast. The weight of the cover glass also slows down the movements of the animals in the water and makes it easier to observe them.

The earth's simplest animals are called protozoa, which really means "first animals" when translated literally. Each protozoan consists of but one cell. Since the cell is the basic unit of which all living things are made, it is hard to think of anything simpler. Protozoa can live successfully with but one such cell unit. Our own bodies are composed of trillions of cells. The protozoan with its single cell can do all of the things that we do to stay alive. This is one of the reasons biologists spend time in observing them. They are simple, and from them we can learn something about the ways in which bigger and more complex living things carry on the business of living.

Protozoa are found in all kinds of water, both fresh and salt. Some even live in the bodies of larger animals. The salt-water types are not always easy to obtain. When they are collected, they are not easy to grow and to keep alive. For this reason the fresh-water types are more commonly used. Every body of fresh water contains many kinds of protozoa, sometimes in very large numbers. When you collect water from a fresh-water source you can set up your own micropond (see Appendix 1). Any drop from such a collection is bound to contain a few types of protozoa, especially one of the larger ones called *Paramecium*. The best magnification to use for looking at it is about 100 times. *Paramecium* is so interesting and exciting an animal that it will serve as a good introduction to the world of life in our drop of water.

Paramecium is big—as protozoa go—but it is not the largest one-celled organism. It moves about constantly and quite rapidly. For this reason it isn't easy to follow it around or to get it to stand still for its photograph. As it moves it takes in food. So long as there is food in the water, it will feed. It sweeps bacteria, small green plants, protozoa smaller than itself, and decaying material into its body.

Paramecium is described as slipper-shaped, and usually swims with its more rounded end forward. If you look closely you will see that there is a special part of the animal which directs the food into the cell body. The food is then collected into a small bubble of water which gets larger and then breaks away and begins to move around through the cell. The bubble of water is the digestive apparatus of

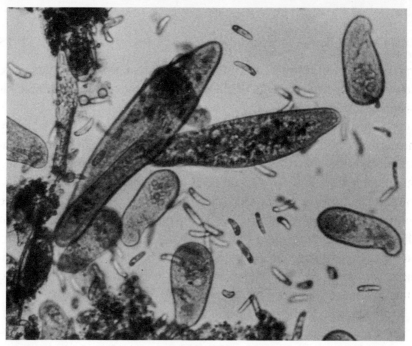

Three common protozoa magnified about 150 ×. The large one is *Paramecium*. The next smaller one is *Colpoda,* while the tiny one is called *Peranema.* These three creatures often appear in artificial micro-ponds.

Seventeen paramecia somehow were quiet long enough for this photo-graph to be made. The tiny hairs by which the animal swims move too fast to be recorded in this photo. (80 ×)

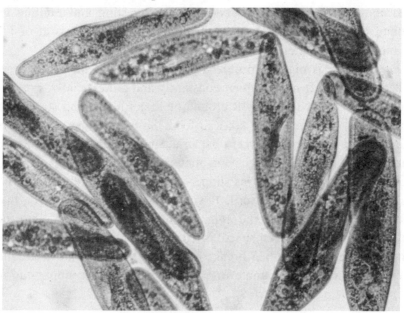

Paramecium magnified about 100 ×. The food canal is visible at the lower left of the animal. Two water pumps (contractile vacuoles) are also shown. The canals which serve the upper water pump are also clearly shown.

Paramecium. It is called a food vacuole. When the animal has much food available there are many bubbles and the body looks dark with the contained food.

The surface of the cell is covered with thousands of tiny beating hairs called cilia. The beating of the cilia moves the animal through the water swiftly and effectively. The groove along which food is directed to the food vacuole is also lined with longer hairs which help push food along. The process of digestion breaks down the larger food molecules into smaller ones which the cell can use. This is what happens in our own stomachs and small intestines.

The large chemical molecules taken in include substances called carbohydrates and proteins. They cannot be used in the form they are taken in by any animal. They must be broken down by digestion into smaller molecules. All carbohydrates are converted into glucose, a simple sugar which is used by both animals and plants for energy. Proteins taken in are changed to amino acids which are used in growth and repair.

Paramecium needs a great deal of energy to propel it in its swift path through the water. It also needs energy to grow and to reproduce more *paramecia.*

Paramecium, like most protozoa, reproduces itself by splitting into two new animals. When it has a rich food supply it grows so fast that it reproduces at least once a day. It does not take long before the offspring of a single paramecium become thousands. Because the one-celled *Paramecium* takes in food, moves, grows, reacts, and reproduces, we call it a living thing—an organism.

There are sure to be other kinds of one-celled animals in a drop of water. There are also some small animals whose bodies consist of many cells. Sometimes they are smaller than *Paramecium.* These many-celled creatures also carry on all the basic actions which the cells in your own body perform. You are an organism with trillions of cells of different types. Each type of cell in your body is a specialist, equipped to do one special job.

You might not agree that these tiny organisms can do all the things you can do. You say that they cannot read this book; they can't think; and they can't kick a football. These are very complex activities. They are based, however, on the simple activities shared by all living things: the ability to take in food, to use that food for energy and growth, and to react to forces in the environment or inside the body.

Paramecium and the other simple organisms in a drop of water react to light or to a change in temperature or to chemicals or touch. Their reactions are always quite simple—they move toward or away from the disturbance. It is a reaction just the same, differing from our own only in degree and complexity.

But how do these tiny organisms influence one another?

One way of looking at life is as a state of organization. The structures and chemicals of living things are organized in such a way as to maintain their vitality and to prevent disorganization. This tendency toward disorganization is found in the nonliving world also. Scientists use the word *entropy* to describe it. The energy expended by living things is used, in part, to maintain organization and prevent entropy.

What is the source of the energy which enables living things to stay alive and to perform the jobs which keep not only the organism but also the type going?

The energy that living things use is obtained from foods, the mixture of chemical molecules in which the energy is stored. All the matter in the universe is composed of ninety-two chemical elements. We say ninety-two because this is the number which occur naturally. Man has been able to make eleven or twelve new elements but these do not now enter the story. The ninety-two natural elements make up rocks and rivers, oceans and air, mountains and the whole world of life. You already are familiar with a number of elements by names. These include carbon, oxygen, lead, iron, hydrogen, nitrogen, gold, and radium. Of the ninety-two different elements, some twenty-five are found in all living things. These twenty-five, along with the remainder, make up the nonliving world.

The smallest bit of an element is called an *atom*. There are, then, at least ninety-two different kinds of atoms. Atoms of most elements can combine with the atoms of many other elements to form chemical *compounds*. There are many thousands of different kinds of chemical compounds. The smallest bit of a chemical compound is a *molecule*.

Water is a compound. Its molecule is constructed from two atoms of hydrogen which are bound to a single oxygen atom. Hydrogen and oxygen are both colorless, invisible gases. When their atoms are joined chemically, they lose their original properties and form the new substance, water, with its own unique properties. The chemist writes the formula for water in a kind of chemical shorthand—H_2O.

The gas, carbon dioxide, has a molecule composed of one atom of carbon chemically attached to two atoms of oxygen (CO_2). Glucose, a simple sugar, is composed of 24 atoms combined in one molecule— 6 atoms of carbon, 12 atoms of hydrogen and 6 atoms of oxygen. The chemist writes it as $C_6H_{12}O_6$.

Animals must get their food in the form of a few kinds of large chemical molecules. They cannot make these large molecules from the simpler ones available to them.

But green plants can use simple molecules and from them make the molecules that serve as the "stuff of life." They do this by combining molecules of water and carbon dioxide to make glucose, the first step in the process of food making. Later they use the glucose so produced to make proteins and other large molecules. Proteins have atoms of nitrogen and often phosphorus in their molecules. Plants obtain these necessary building blocks from minerals called nitrates and phosphates.

Chlorophyll, the green material in plants, plays an interesting as well as indispensable part in food manufacture. It enables the plant to use energy from the sun in the process of *photosynthesis,* as this food-producing activity is called. Glucose then serves as the starting point for the manufacture of all the more complex molecules needed to support life. The sun's energy flows into the world of life through the green plants.

All living things get energy for their life-supporting activities by burning, or oxidizing, food materials which contain carbon in their molecules; these materials are usually glucose. They give off the gas carbon dioxide as a waste of the energy-yielding process. The carbon dioxide given off as a waste product by water organisms dissolves easily in the water. Carbon dioxide from the atmosphere also dissolves in surface waters, since it is a very soluble substance. This increases the supply of this vital gas available for the plants that live in fresh and salt water.

There is about eighty times as much carbon dioxide dissolved in the waters that cover most of the earth's surface as there is in the atmosphere above the earth. One result of this fact is that the major amount of photosynthesis takes place in water. It has been estimated that water plants produce from 80 to 85 per cent of the food made by photosynthesis.

What goes on in the green plant cell when it is making food? It is now known that photosynthesis is a complex process with many intricate steps. Only a few of these steps have been explained. The rest are being intensively investigated by hundreds of scientists the world over.

For a long time it has been known that green plants give off oxygen gas as a by-product of photosynthesis. The release of oxygen in the food-making process provides an important illustration of the interrelationship of all living things in all environments, including a drop of water. Most plants and animals need oxygen for the process in which they burn foods to get energy. The oxygen is made available by green plants. Sunlight was the plant's energy source to run its photosynthetic machine. It was then transformed to chemical energy in the plant. When animals feed on plants, or on animals which have fed on plants, they obtain this chemical energy in the form of the food they take in. This energy is now used to operate their living machinery. Most plants and animals give off carbon dioxide as a waste product.

Green plants get back from these plants and animals the carbon dioxide they need to make glucose. They give off oxygen in using the carbon dioxide. There is thus a cycling of oxygen and carbon dioxide between plants and animals in which these chemicals travel in what seems an endless journey. No wonder the supply of these chemicals does not run out.

Plants thus serve as the basis of all life in a drop of water as well as of all life in oceans, seas, lakes, ponds, and streams. They alone can make food from simple chemical molecules.

One way of looking at life in fresh or salt water is as a series of food chains. The beginning of a chain consists of hundreds or thousands of individual plants even in a small drop of water, and of trillions upon trillions of them that teem in large bodies of water. They are the *producers* and as such they support all life in their environment. Plants are eaten by microscopic and larger animals in the same waters. Plant eaters are called first-level *consumers*. Larger animals in the same waters feed on the smaller ones and are thus second-level consumers. There may even be third- and fourth-level consumers. As we move along a chain the number of individual organisms gets smaller and smaller. At the end of a chain there are a few or even a single living animal; a codfish, a sulfur-bottom whale or a tiger shark.

All consumers give off a variety of waste products which accumulate in the environment along with the bodies of dead plants and animals. These could be harmful to the living if they continued to accumulate. Besides, the atoms and molecules of which their bodies are composed are removed from the world of life which needs them. They are not available in limitless supply.

Most living things are not equipped to use these waste materials and dead bodies as they pile up. There is a group of organisms in all environments that can unlock this chemical wealth and return it in a form which can be used by living organisms. They are called *re-ducers* and include bacteria, molds, and scavenger organisms. They are essential to the producer and consumer organisms.

Every part of a food chain is important. If one organism is removed from a chain, the entire chain is affected. If the producers disappear for some reason, all the consumers will follow them unless they can find another food source. If they feed on producers in another chain they will disrupt the new chain and upset the balance of life in it.

The organisms in water are probably part of a number of different chains which are connected in an even more delicately balanced web of life. One living type in such a web may be so important that if anything happens to it the whole web will be violently affected.

Our drops of water are a way of looking at all kinds of larger bodies of water and the life in them. We have looked at some of the facts needed to understand and interpret the facts. And these facts can be applied to any kind of environment.

Chapter 2

ANTONY VAN LEEUWENHOEK AND HIS LITTLE ANIMALS

Antony van Leeuwenhoek was born in Delft, Holland, in 1632, and lived most of his long life in this prosperous seaport. Leeuwenhoek was not a scientist by profession. He was a successful businessman, whose education was a fairly simple one. It would be hard to imagine that this would be the kind of training for becoming a major discoverer of a new field. But this is exactly what Leeuwenhoek did.

Leeuwenhoek had a shop in which he sold linens, woolens, and other kinds of cloth. One instrument he used in his work was a small magnifying glass called a linen counter, which is really a small, simple microscope. It makes things look bigger. The quality of cloth depends on the closeness with which threads of different materials are woven. And Leeuwenhoek used this device to count the threads in the cloth he sold.

Magnifying glasses had been produced long before the 1600s. Some unknown discoverer or discoverers had found that pieces of glass curved in a special way could make things look bigger. It was not until the 1300s that this idea was used in a practical way. About this time men began to make eyeglasses from pieces of glass which they learned to grind to the right curvature. About fifty years before Leeuwenhoek's birth some men were making microscopes and telescopes from combinations of lenses. They used two or more lenses in a tube. How much these men saw when they used their glasses as microscopes we do not know for sure, since they left little information about this.

Leeuwenhoek became interested in lenses and began to grind them as a hobby. We think that he did get some instruction from an eyeglass maker. There were many such men in Delft grinding lenses for their living. Leeuwenhoek used gold, silver, and brass to mount the lenses he made so he could use them as microscopes. His lenses were very small, but skillfully ground. About 10 of the 250 he made in his lifetime can be seen today in museums. The rest have disappeared. How much more we would know if they were available.

The microscopes have been studied by modern scientists who are experts in optics. They found them to be excellent instruments. The microscope on page 25 was one of his best ones. It had the lens mounted between two thin sheets of silver. A small hole drilled through the silver held the tiny lens in place. The center of the small lens served as the microscope. A few thumbscrews on the back of the silver plates were used to hold an object to be viewed and to move it close to or away from the lens.

When Leeuwenhoek looked through his microscope he had to hold it very close to his eye. It also had to face some strong source of light so that he could see the object properly.

Some of his microscopes were so constructed that he could examine the tail of a live goldfish or tadpole. Others were built so he could look at tiny glass tubes filled with water from many places.

Whatever he looked at was usually being seen for the first time. He made wonderful lenses which magnified things from 40 times to as much as 270 times. In 1933, a scientist in Holland used the microscope shown on page 25 to photograph some tiny objects. In the illustration on page 26 you can see one of these photographs. It is the shell of a plant which measures about one-thousandth of an inch across. Below it is a photograph of the same kind of shell made with a modern, expensive microscope. It is amazing how clear and sharp are the images seen through Leeuwenhoek's microscope when compared with lenses made up of seven or eight separate glass sections.

One thing that bothers us a little today about this unusual man is that he would tell no one, not even his closest friends, how he made his microscopes, how he ground his lenses, or even how he used the

Another Leeuwenhoek microscope shown one and three-quarters actual size. This one is part of the collection of the Utrecht University Museum in Holland. This is the microscope used in 1933 to photograph the diatom shell shown on page 26. *(Courtesy of Dr. J. G. van Cittert-Eymers)*

microscopes. He tells us as much when he said, "My methods for seeing the very smallest animals and minute eels, I do not impart to others; nor how to see very many animals at one time. That I keep for myself alone." Although Leeuwenhoek was very secretive about how he did his work, we are very fortunate that he did not keep to himself what he saw.

Leeuwenhoek was an amazingly patient man. He spent many hours daily for over sixty years in making and using microscopes. Fortunately, he was blessed with unusually sharp eyesight and rare good health. How else could he have peered through such tiny lenses for so long and seen so much with such accuracy? He was, in addition, a most original man. He also had fine manipulative skills and was a skillful worker with both glass and metals.

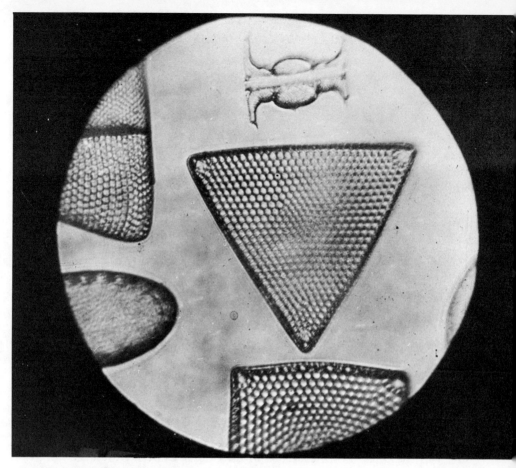

A triangular diatom shell photographed in 1933 with the original Leeuwenhoek microscope shown on page 25. (*Courtesy of Dr. J. G. van Cittert-Eymers*)

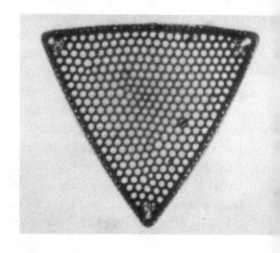

A photograph of the same species of diatom made with a fine modern microscope and magnified about 100 ×. What do you think of Leeuwenhoek's microscope and its performance?

Leeuwenhoek investigated what he saw with great care and skill. He managed to avoid allowing his imagination to control what he saw and described in his letters. It is not difficult to recognize many of the animals and plants he described even though there were no names for them. He could only describe them by their shape, color, size, the way they moved, and then by preparing drawings of what he saw. These he left for us in about 345 letters he wrote to the members of the Royal Society of England—the group of scientists with whom he carried on his correspondence.

Leeuwenhoek looked at everything he could find. He described what he saw with words and with drawings. He looked at parts of insects and at the blood from a number of kinds of animals. He saw both blood tubes and blood cells. He examined waters of every type.

Leeuwenhoek discovered the world of microscopic life. He was the first to see protozoa—the one-celled animals—and bacteria—plants which he called "little animals."

The most famous of his letters is the one in which he described what we now know to be bacteria. It was written in 1683. In this famous letter he described what he saw in some saliva which he took from his mouth after very carefully brushing his teeth with coarse salt. He mixed a little saliva with rain water. To assure the members of the Royal Society that there were no animals in the water, he states that he examined it carefully. His letter went on:

"I then most always saw, with great wonder, that in the said matter there were many very little 'animalcules,' very prettily a-moving. The biggest sort had the shape of Fig. A. These had a very strong and swift motion, and shot through the water (or spittle) like a pike does through the water. These were most always few in number. The second sort had the shape of Fig. B. These ofttimes spun round like a top, and every now and then took a course like that shown between C and D: and these were far more in number.

"To the third sort I could assign no figure for at times they seemed to be oblong, while anon they looked perfectly round. These were so small that I could see them no bigger than Fig. E: yet therewithal they went ahead so nimbly and hovered so together that you might imagine them to be a big swarm of gnats or flies, flying in and out among one another."

In 1692 he returned to the question of the animals which he

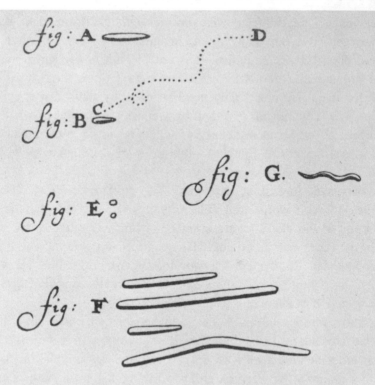

LEEUWENHOEK'S FIGURES OF BACTERIA FROM THE HUMAN MOUTH

Drawings of bacteria by Leeuwenhoek to accompany his Letter No. 17. There is little doubt that Leeuwenhoek drew what he saw and that he observed most accurately.

found in his mouth when he examined his saliva. He again provided drawings of the objects he saw, and scientists today have no trouble in recognizing exactly the kinds of creatures that Leeuwenhoek found.

This genius also examined rain water and water from marshes and swamps, as well as water that had been allowed to stand in tubs exposed to the air. He found many kinds of protozoa which he described in his quaint way, since there was no scientific language with which they could be described more accurately. He was the first to measure the size of tiny things. To do this, he used convenient objects, such as grains of sand or a hair from his head, as a basis for comparison. He made unusually accurate estimates of the size of the creatures he was seeing.

We do know what Leeuwenhoek saw. In his letters to the Royal Society in England, written in his native Dutch, he told the members of his many observations. Someone in the society had to translate the letters into English, but Leeuwenhoek's descriptions of the things he saw so excited these people that word of his accomplishments began to reach all parts of Europe. Many great people, including the royalty of several countries, visited Delft just for the chance to look through one of the microscopes.

Leeuwenhoek lived a long and productive life. He died in 1723 in his ninety-first year. He was looking through his microscopes a few weeks before he died—still able to see things clearly and write about them so that others could understand.

Let us pretend to make ourselves so small that we can enter this drop of water and move around with all the living things that swarm in the drop. We should be able to live like one of these creatures, to make our way through the drop, and really to see what it is like to be a protozoan.

As we plunge into the drop we find we are in a very busy place. There is much going on all around us. Some creatures rush by or bump into us. Others crawl or glide by in a leisurely way. When we get our bearings and can look more closely we see that the protozoa do not all move in the same way.

Paramecium, which we looked at before, is one of the fast ones. It is shaped something like a cigar, and the whole animal is covered with thousands of tiny hairs called cilia. Here is one swimming by. Its cilia are moving in unison. They look like so many thousands of oars all pulling together. No wonder it moves so swiftly and so smoothly. Imagine what would happen if they did not move together.

The front end is rounded. The pointed end is usually the trailing one. *Paramecium* has may relatives which also move by cilia. Here is one coming toward us now. It is bigger than *Paramecium* and is colored a delicate pink. It has a strange and unfamiliar name, *Blepharisma*. It does not move as fast as *Paramecium*. Most of its hairs are much longer than those of *Paramecium*. It swims gracefully through the water and as it swims along it sweeps food into an opening which leads deep inside the animal.

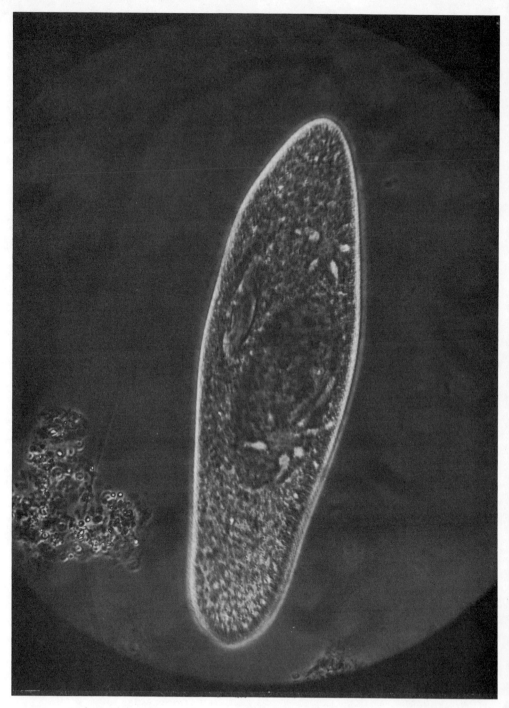

A single living *Paramecium* magnified about 146 ×. The two water pumps are visible to the right, each with its canals. The food canal is visible to the left, while the large dark oval body is the larger of the animal's two nuclei.

Here is a small piece of decaying matter. An unusual creature is attached to it. It stretches out in the shape of a trumpet or horn. Colored bluish-green, it has cilia, and is a relative of *Paramecium* and *Blepharisma*. It is called *Stentor*. Most of its cilia are very long

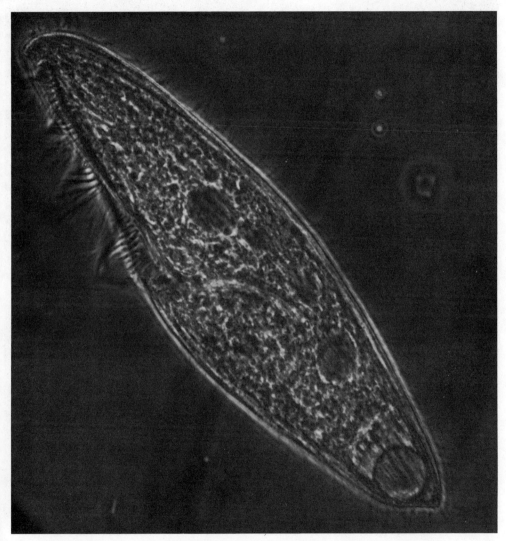

The pink protozoan, *Blepharisma*, shown at about 150 magnifications. The long, beating hairs (cilia) are shown, slightly blurred because they were moving rapidly. The single water pump is the circular structure at the back end of the animal.

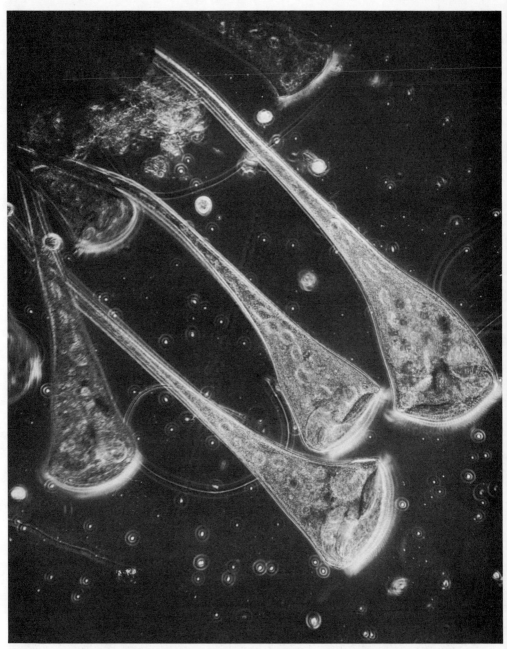

Four blue-green stentors, attached at their narrow ends and fully extended in their typical trumpet shape (70 ×). Note the beaded structure
in the middle of the animal. This is the nucleus. The long cilia at the
broad end were beating so fast they did not photograph clearly, but
they can be seen.

and are found around the wide end of the animal. They beat so fast that they set up whirlpools which pull food into the animal.

The name *Stentor* was given to this animal by the man who first saw it. Its trumpet shape recalled for him the herald of ancient Greece whose voice was so loud it could be heard for great distances.

But now *Stentor* has collapsed almost in the shape of a ball. It has let go of its hold on the decaying material and is rapidly swimming away. If we can keep up with it we will see that it will soon settle down again. It will attach itself to something solid and slowly begin to stretch out in the shape of a trumpet.

What happens when another animal bumps into a *Stentor?* We'll watch for a while. Here comes one. Its body touches *Stentor* and the *Stentor* pulls itself together and is less than one-fourth its stretched-out size. It contracts. Slowly it begins to get longer once more.

Blepharisma behaves in a different way when it is touched. It backs away and moves off in a slightly different direction. It tries to avoid obstacles. *Paramecium* behaves the way *Blepharisma* does. It swims away from other creatures it touches or from solid objects in its path.

Paramecium, Blepharisma, and *Stentor* are protozoa which move swiftly by means of their many cilia. But this is not the only way in which protozoa can move. Nor are these three organisms the only ones we might see which have cilia. There are thousands of other animals with swimming hairs.

Yet another kind of protozoan is one which moves very, very slowly. To observe this one we will have to swim down to the bottom of the drop. This new kind of one-celled animal moves by crawling along some surface—the mud on a pond bottom, the leaves of a water plant, some decaying material—anything which is solid and has a surface that can be used for support. This animal moves when its inner substance flows along and pushes out temporary "feet" in the direction it is moving. The animal keeps changing its shape as it moves. The false feet which pull it along are called *pseudopodia.* They are also used by these animals in capturing food. When touched or disturbed, pseudopodia react by rolling the animal up into a ball. If they are not soon disturbed they begin to form again as the inside of the animal begins to flow once more. There are many relatives of this

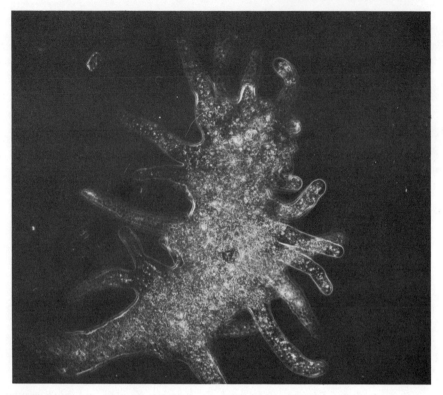

A very large ameba (50 ×) with many pseudopods.

animal, *Ameba,* which also move and capture their food with false feet.

As we swim around through our drop we are bound to bump into another kind of protozoan. This one has one or more long whiplike structures attached to the front end of the animal. Each of these whips is called a *flagellum*. They may be 10, 15, or even 20 times as long as cilia. The animal moves by lashing its flagellum back and forth. This pulls the animal forward. Many of the animals that move this way are green, containing the chemical chlorophyll which we associate with plants.

One of the most common of these is *Euglena,* which has puzzled us for years. We cannot decide whether it is plant or animal. In a way it is both. Its chlorophyll makes it able to produce its own food. When there is no light for a long time, the green color disappears

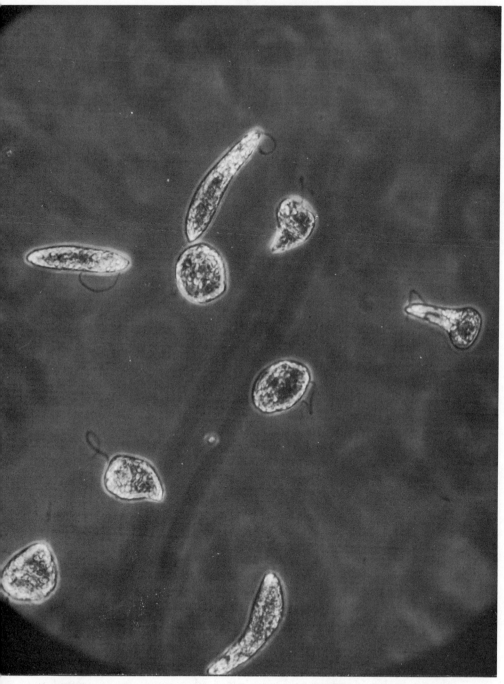

Euglena, the unusual protozoan with plantlike abilities. Its locomotor apparatus is a single long whip or flagellum.

and the organism must get its food ready-made. This it does by absorbing materials from the water through its outer skin. It is a kind of scavenger at this time, since the materials it takes in are decaying substances.

Here is one approaching with a bright red spot gleaming near its front end. This red structure is sensitive to light; it is a simple eye and very necessary to the organism. Of course, *Euglena*, to produce its chlorophyll, must have light, and it always swims toward light. If our drop of water is lighted from one side, the *Euglena* will move toward the lighted side. It is drawn there by its flagellum but led to it by the eyespot, which reacts to light.

There are many other animals with flagella which are likely to be in the drop of water.

It might help put order in all the things we have just seen, if we look at the protozoa in a little more systematic way. Protozoa are the simplest organisms alive on the earth today, since most of them consist of but a single cell—that is, a single unit of living substance. The one cell has a *nucleus* which controls its actions. The nucleus is surrounded by the rest of the living material. It is bounded by a wall or *membrane*. Some of them even have a type of protective skeleton, but most of them do not.

It would seem as though one cell is as simple as a living thing can be. This is true, yet over thirty thousand different types or species of one-celled animals are known to be alive on the earth today.

How big are protozoa? We must make use of a different scale of measurement to answer this question. The unit is called a *micron*. It takes 1000 microns to stretch to a length of one millimeter! If a protozoan is 100 microns in length we would have to place ten of them end to end to measure one millimeter. Twenty-five thousand microns placed end to end make up one whole inch.

Some of the smallest protozoans measure no more than two or three microns in length. The biggest ones are as much as 1000 microns long—a full millimeter. We can see most protozoa without using lenses, but they will only appear to us as tiny specks in the water.

We know that the protozoa must get food. Since food is not always to be found in the same place, they must move around to get it. Once the food is taken into the body the larger food particles must be changed into smaller units so that they can be used. Protozoans use the materials they take in to give them energy and to provide them with materials for growing and for making new individuals like themselves.

The materials they use for energy give up their energy only if oxygen gas is available. All waters contain some gaseous oxygen in a dissolved form. This oxygen flows into the cell through the enclosing membrane of the animal's surface.

Whenever living things use food in their life activities they give off waste materials. These must be expelled from the body.

Protozoa must be able to react to the things around them. If they could not swim away quickly from a harmful situation they might not survive. All fresh-water protozoa have another problem: their cells keep taking in water all the time. The piling up of this water would cause them to burst if it continued. But they do not burst. They have a special structure—the *contractile vacuole*—to avoid this calamity.

The *Ameba* is one of the best known of all the protozoa. It is a very easy animal to watch because it moves so slowly. This is the way it was described, over two hundred years ago, by the naturalist Rosel von Rosenhof after he saw a particle of jelly sticking to the inside of a glass container of water and weeds. It moved and this attracted his attention. He said, "It fastened itself on the side of the glass and since, like animals, it moves, altho very slowly, from place to place, and thereby continually alters its form, and as I frequently examined the water with a magnifying glass, the creature was necessarily discovered and, as soon as I touched it, it contracted itself into a sphere and fell to the bottom."

Rosel noticed that as it moved the animal continually changed its shape. For this reason he named it *Proteus* after the monster in a fable who was able to assume all kinds of shapes and forms. Later the name was changed to *Ameba,* and *Ameba proteus,* as the animal is now called, is one of the commonest of all fresh-water protozoa.

Ameba moves so slowly that we might not even think that it is alive. Let us touch one lightly as we swim by it. *Ameba* reacts by rolling up into a ball. Slowly it will begin to show signs of life. The inside of the body contains many dark grains of different sizes as well

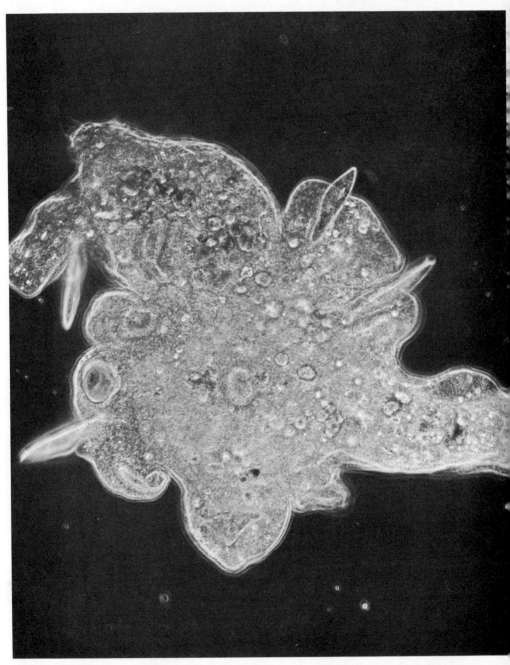

A large ameba in the process of reducing the population of paramecia. Four paramecia are seen being engulfed. Three others were taken in while the animal was being focused for photography. It took about fifteen seconds for the entire process. (70 ×)

as lighter-colored bubbles of some substance. These flow inside the cell as one or more false feet are pushed out.

Ameba captures its food by flowing around it. Two or more false feet surround some bacteria, some decaying matter, or a small, slow-moving protozoan and enclose them in a little bubble of water. The prey is now inside the cell in the bubble. It is a food bubble and is separated from the cell contents by a membrane. Inside this food bubble, *Ameba* digests the food—breaks it down chemically into particles small enough to pass through the skin and into its body.

Once while observing a giant species of *Ameba* under the microscope, I added a drop of water containing many paramecia. I was startled by what I saw. Apparently this *Ameba* found each *Paramecium* a desirable form of food.

When a paramecium bumped into an ameba, pseudopods began to

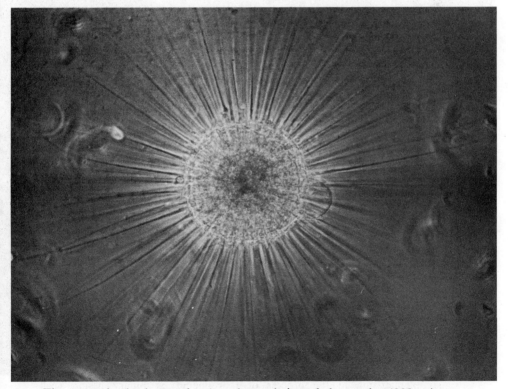

The sun animal, *Actinosphaerium*, is a relative of the ameba (200 ×). The single water pump is about ready to squeeze out its surplus water by contracting. The pseudopods are slender and are supported by stiff rods.

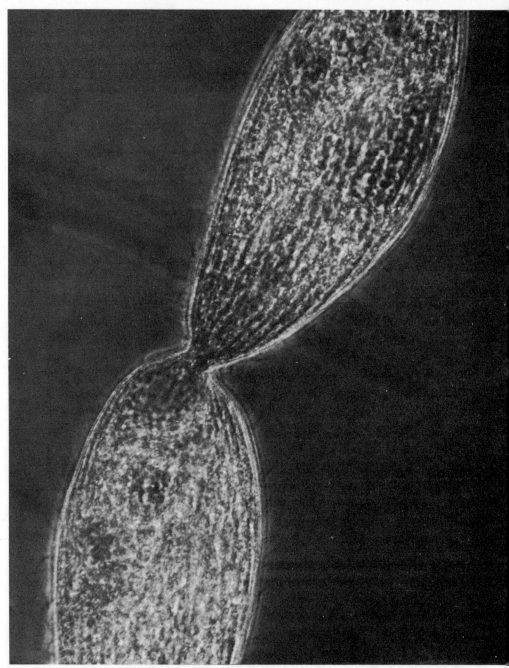

A blepharisma in the process of reproducing by binary fission (cell division). About two minutes later, two new blepharisma moved their separate ways. (250 ×)

form quickly and in less than half a minute the *Paramecium* was sealed in a food vacuole. Why didn't the *Paramecium* swim away?

Then another one touched the *Ameba*. I saw that the *Ameba* seemed to excrete a substance which held the prey close to it, while its pseudopods engulfed it. In a short time there were seven food vacuoles, each containing a *Paramecium*.

There is a single large, clear bubble in each *Ameba*. Sometimes it suddenly disappears. If we keep looking, we see that it begins to form again—and again disappears. This happens about once a minute. It is a contracting bubble and when it disappears it has squeezed out the surplus water. This is the way *Ameba,* as well as all other fresh-water protozoa, solve the problem of too much water. The water bubble is a type of living pump and is important to these animals. It helps keep them alive.

When there is a large amount of food, *Ameba* keeps taking it in. It then grows very fast and reproduces itself. An ameba can grow just so large and then it becomes two. The nucleus divides into two nuclei. The rest of the cell then pinches in and two amebae are formed, each with its own nucleus and one-half of the rest of the cell.

The new amebae formed are able to live their own lives at once. They move, take in food, grow, react, and very soon they reproduce. This, then, is part of the story of simple living things. They are born. They feed and grow. They reproduce their kind. It is an endless cycle.

The protozoan, *Blepharisma,* is a large one. It is about 600 microns long and is pink in color. It is slower moving than *Paramecium* and is easy for us to follow around. Its long cilia sweep it through the water quite gracefully.

Blepharisma feeds on smaller protozoa. The animals it does capture are swept into a food vacuole and swim around in it until the digestive juices kill it. They cannot escape since the membrane of the bubble is tough.

One large type of *Blepharisma* is a cannibal. It feeds on smaller *Blepharisma*. It can be recognized because it is a much deeper red than other kinds.

Blepharisma seems to be the favorite food of *Stentor*. In the laboratory we grow *Stentor* by feeding it on *Blepharisma*. *Stentor* can stretch its body five or six times its relaxed size. It does this when it is attached. This is when it resembles a horn.

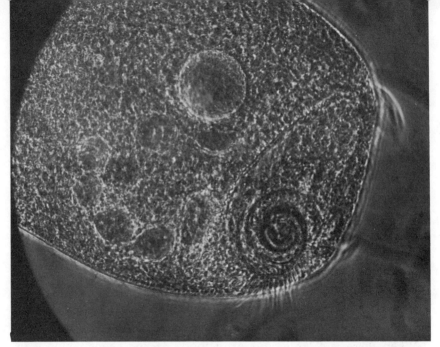

The trumpet end of a stentor. A few of the long cilia whose beating sets up currents of water carrying food into the animal can be seen. The water pump and part of the beaded nucleus are also visible. The coiled structure is part of the food-getting apparatus. (200 ×)

Vorticella, the "bell-animal," is a small protozoan with a long stalk. It often attaches itself to the bodies of larger animals and gets a free ride. A copepod, a small crustacean of ocean plankton, is covered by over fifty vorticellae, which slows his movements considerably. This type of *Vorticella* has a stalk which the animal can contract to pull its bell down quickly. (50 ×)

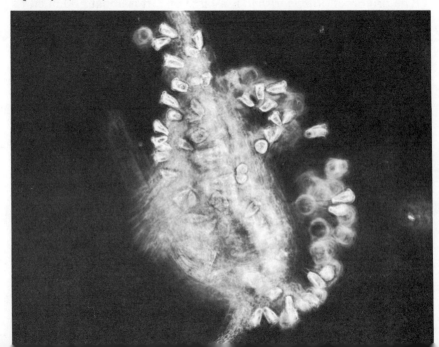

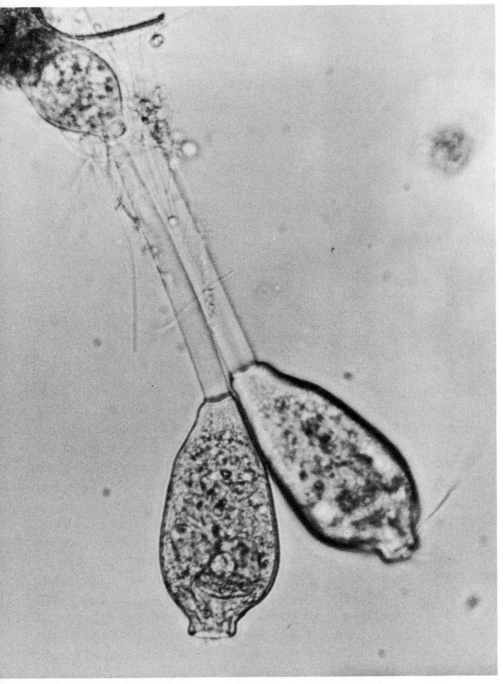

Another stalked protozoan, this one from fresh water. The stalk of this animal is not contractile. (200 ✕)

Vorticella is called the bell animal. It is unusual in appearance. The body is small and shaped like a tiny bell. The cilia are found around the mouth of the bell, and at the other end, each bell is attached to a long stalk. The stalk is usually fixed to something solid in the water.

Vorticella is usually found in large clusters. There may be hundreds or even thousands of individuals in what looks like a small forest. The bell is the working part of each animal. It captures food. The cilia sweep food into the bell in tiny currents of water they create. When the bells are touched, they suddenly disappear. A close look tells us that the stalk has contracted like a corkscrew and pulled the bell down. Slowly the stalk unwinds and extends the bell again.

Euglena is quite small—about 25 microns long. It swims by means of its one flagellum. We are quite sure that Leeuwenhoek saw *Euglena*. In one of his letters he described a creature as "green in the middle and before, and behind white."

We will call *Euglena* an animal even though we know that it contains chlorophyll and that it can function as a plant. But it behaves as an animal and this is what interests us now.

Euglena grows so fast that if we had a small jar containing some euglenae and kept it in a well-lighted place, the jar would soon look green with the millions upon millions of *Euglena* which would have ideal conditions for their growth. We can even see how this animal moves toward the light by putting the jar in a position where the light enters from one side. In a few hours, the lighted side would be deep green in color while the other side is not colored at all. All euglenae move toward the light.

Euglena is used in medical work with human beings. Euglenae, like all other living things, need vitamins. One vitamin that humans must get in their diet is vitamin B_{12}, which our body uses to make hemoglobin. This is the red chemical in our blood which carries the oxygen we need. If we do not get enough B_{12}, a kind of anemia develops. This disease can be cured by supplying the missing vitamin. There is one problem: there are many other types of anemia in man, and it is not easy to decide what kind of anemia a person has.

This is where *Euglena* enters the story. It is sensitive to one part of the vitamin in one trillion parts of water. This is more sen-

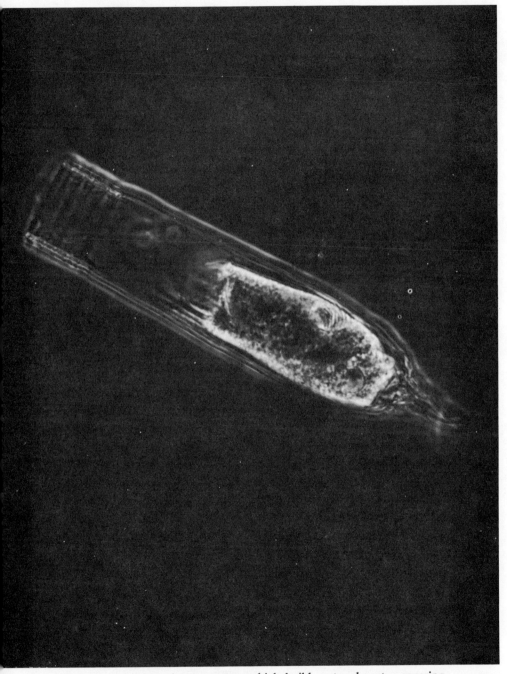

A strange type of marine protozoan which builds a tough outer covering. The animal within has just contracted; usually it fills the whole case. This one, called a tintinnid, was found attached to a crab larva. (250 ×)

sitive than any method we have of finding this tiny amount of B_{12}. *Euglena* needs B_{12} to thrive. We can raise the animal in the laboratory and give it all the conditions it needs. When vitamin B_{12} is missing, there are few euglenae in the growing tubes.

When a doctor suspects that one of his patients has vitamin B_{12} deficiency anemia he can quickly make sure. He takes a small sample of blood and adds the blood fluid to a tube containing *Euglena*. He then uses another tube with the same amount of *Euglena* and adds everything the animal needs, including B_{12}. One day later, the two tubes are compared. If both tubes show the same amount of *Euglena* the doctor decides that the anemia was not caused by a lack of vitamin B_{12}. If the tube with blood has fewer euglenae (is lighter in color), he knows that the blood had little B_{12}. The disease is then easy to treat.

This story of *Euglena* is told here to show that the protozoa are not as different from the larger animals as we might have thought. They are as alive as we are. They have the same basic needs and they satisfy these needs in the same basic ways. They also make it possible for us to use these very simple living things in experiments to find out more about ourselves and about them, too, of course.

Chapter 3

THE DIATOMS—FLOATING JEWELS

All of the life on earth depends upon the ability of green plants to make food. Much of the land surface of the earth is covered with plants of many varieties. The waters that make up over 70 per cent of the earth's surface also teem with plant life. Fresh and salt waters contain all the plants needed to support a tremendous population of animals—both microscopic and macroscopic. Indirectly they also contribute much of the food that we need.

Land plants are easy to see; they dominate so many landscapes. In forests, woods, and jungle they are both imposing and impressive. The plant life of oceans, seas, lakes, and ponds is not so easy to see. Most of it consists of microscopic living things. Actually, seaweeds, the large algae living in the ocean, are a minor source of food.

How much food do the plants of land and water produce? The question is much too difficult even to make an educated guess. But a few scientists have tried to make an estimate. They based it on a few measurable factors, especially the amount of carbon dioxide not only in the atmosphere but also dissolved in the surface waters.

The amount of material produced is so huge it almost defies our imagination. Try, in some way, to picture how big a pile of foodstuff this quantity would make. It is close to one thousand billion (1,000,000,000,000) tons of starches, sugars, proteins, and oils which support life on the earth. Multiplying the number of tons by two thousand gives us a figure of two million billion (2,000,000,000,000,000) pounds.

Almost all (over 80 per cent) of this unimaginable amount of food is made by tiny plants which live in the water. Most of these individual plants are so small that a microscope must be used to see them. When they are made visible we find that they are diatoms. Diatoms are not familiar to most people because they are so small, and they are rarely seen except by microscopists (people who work with microscopes). Even the name of these plants sounds strange and unfamiliar.

Diatoms are one-celled green plants. Actually they do not look green—most of them look yellow or brownish-yellow. This is so because the green chlorophyll they contain is masked by other chemicals which are yellow and brown.

Diatoms are found in such fantastically large numbers in water that they often color the water in which they are growing. Fishermen who catch the large numbers of fish we use as food have a colorful way of describing the way diatoms look to them in large numbers. They say the water looks like "Dutchman's 'baccy juice." They also know that where diatoms are found in such large numbers they somehow do not find the fish they are looking for. Most fish do not feed on diatoms directly. But other kinds of animals, smaller than fish, do. After they have grazed the diatom-rich pastures they move out to surrounding areas. It is here that the fishermen locate the fish they catch.

The name diatom means "cut in two." They are found wherever there is water and some light. They are found in fresh waters from sea level to those on mountain sides up to 10,000 feet above sea level. The diatoms found in salt waters flourish from the poles to warm tropical seas. Some diatoms can even do well in the very high temperatures of the water of hot springs such as "Old Faithful" in Yellowstone Park.

Each diatom is a complete and independent living thing, and may be anywhere from 4 microns to about 500 microns across. Most of the types are from 25 to 200 microns. This would be from $\frac{1}{25}$ of an inch for the large ones to about $\frac{1}{1000}$ of an inch for the small ones.

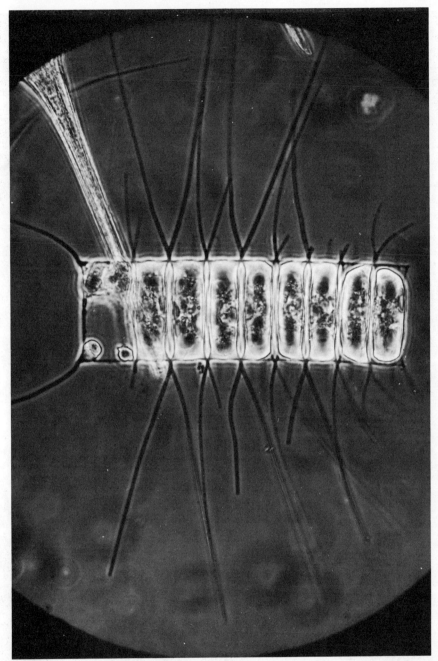

Chaetoceras, a common diatom of the marine plankton. This one is a colony of individual plants (nine in this colony) attached end to end. Each plant is a complete organism. The living plant structures obscure the glassy shell in which the living substance is contained. (200 ×)

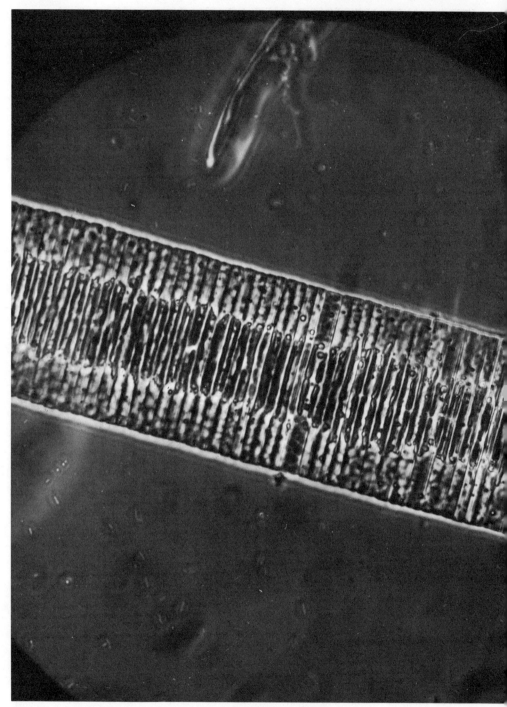

Fragillaria, a colonial fresh-water diatom. (200 ×)

When we look at them with a microscope, the living diatom cell looks something like the cells of the higher plants. There is a network of the living substance which appears to contain many small grains. It also contains some small bodies colored brownish-green. We would expect to find bodies with chlorophyll, since these are the structures which manufacture food for the plant. Each diatom also has a large nucleus. This is to be expected even if we cannot easily see it. The nucleus controls all life activities in diatoms as it does in other cells—and it functions in cell reproduction.

What is really unusual in the diatom is its outer covering. The wall is composed of a chemical called silicon. This is the same chemical found in glass and in sand. The living cell absorbs this chemical from the waters in which it lives. With silicon it builds a covering shell of great beauty. The shells are shaped in various forms, most of them being circular, triangular, or oval. In addition they have finer markings which form designs of unusual attractiveness. They are tiny glass boxes. It is no exaggeration to call them living jewels.

The glass case of each plant resembles a small pillbox. One-half of the case is slightly smaller than the other, which fits over it rather tightly. These shells are very hard and quite tough. Long after the living material has disappeared, the shells drift slowly to the bottom and pile up there in the soft ooze on the bottom of bodies of water.

You might think a living thing so simple would not show much variety in its structure, but no fewer than fifteen thousand different varieties have been found, described, and named. Most salt-water diatoms are circular, oval, or show regular geometric shapes with a definite number of sides (three, four, or sometimes more). The fresh-water kinds are usually boat-shaped.

It is the appearance of the fine markings of the surface of the shells which gives them their reputation for beauty. These are fine and intricate. Some of them are arranged in patterns that are both complex and attractive. The markings are formed when the cell deposits more or less silicon and makes these markings thick or thin. Sometimes the shell has tiny openings in a regular pattern. Some of the markings are so fine that they are used to test microscope lenses. Only a good lens will reveal the finest markings. Experienced microscopists take along slides with some diatoms shells to see how

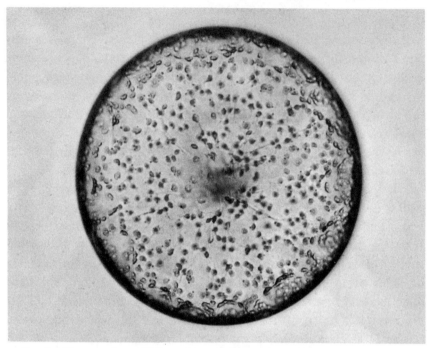

Coscinodiscus, a large diatom, very common in ocean waters.
A.   Top view showing the many chloroplasts.
B.   Side view of the same plant. It clearly shows the pillbox structure with two overlapping halves of the glass outer shell. (Both 400 ×)

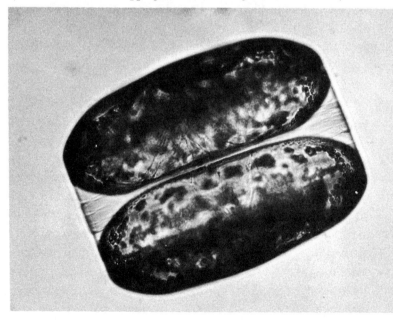

well the microscope lenses they are interested in perform.

The complicated designs produced by the markings on the shells are found in a particular kind of diatom—generation after generation after generation. This suggests that these markings are inherited just as we inherit our eye color, our hair color, or our body build.

Diatoms reproduce very rapidly by the simplest of methods—cell division, or fission. The living material in the cell is divided into two equal amounts. The division of the nucleus occurs at the same time.

The two halves of the pillbox shell separate and move apart as the living material inside grows. At the same time, two new half-shells are gradually formed. When the new glass cases are completed, the two new diatoms separate and carry on individual lives. Each new diatom has one of its shell halves from the old diatom and a

A jewel-like arrangement of thirty-eight diatom shells. A different type of lighting produces pictures with this appearance. (50 ×)

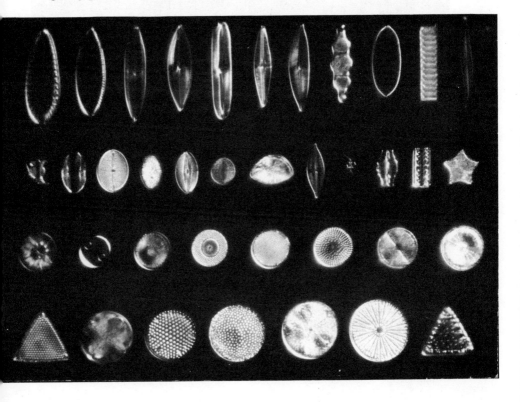

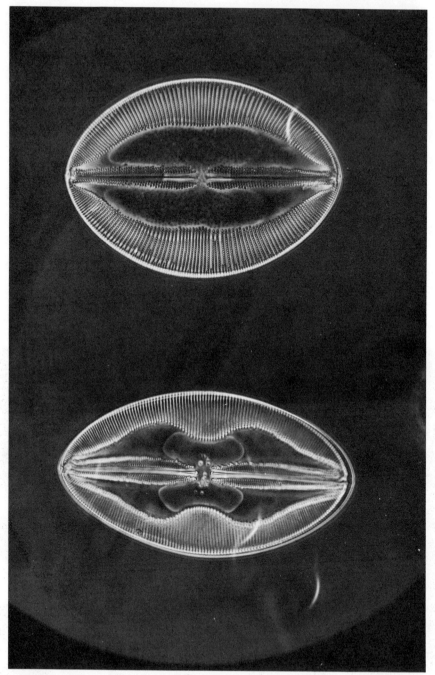

Fine markings of two oval-shaped diatom shells (300 ×). Other types of shells have markings so delicate and fine that they test the abilities of microscope lenses at magnifications of 1000 × and more.

new one. The new half-shell in each is smaller than the old one and lies inside it.

So, over many generations, half of the new diatoms are getting smaller and smaller. This, obviously, cannot continue too long. But at certain periods a new kind of structure is formed. At this time both halves of the pillbox are discarded. The enlarged body of living material produces complete new shells larger than the old ones. No one knows just how this happens or what causes it to happen. It is one of the many unanswered scientific questions.

Diatoms do not multiply at the same frequency all through the year. In the waters of the North Atlantic there is a very interesting reproduction pattern. The numbers of diatoms fluctuate. As their numbers change, they affect the animal life in the same waters. In the winter, the number of animals and plants present in the plankton of these waters is at its low point. By March or April, as the sun's rays become stronger and the surface waters have warmed, the plants, especially the diatoms, suddenly burst forth in their living activities. They multiply at a fantastic rate. A single cell will give rise to one hundred in a week and as many as ten thousand by the end of the next week. The surface waters become greenish-brown as the trillions upon trillions of cells flourish under conditions which are now ideal for them.

By early summer the diatoms are not as numerous, but the animals of the plankton and the larger animals which feed on diatoms and plankton animals begin to multiply—with so much food available.

By summer's end, the number of diatoms in these waters is rather small. It was this fact that surprised scientists. They thought that increased intensity of sunlight and the warming of the waters produced continuing ideal conditions for diatom growth.

The sun's rays become less strong and the air temperature goes lower in early fall. A second explosion of diatom reproduction, not as great as the one in the spring, takes place. By the time winter returns, the number of diatoms has again been reduced by the animals in the plankton and the arrival of spring is needed to start the cycle over again.

This cycle is a complex one. It took many years to unravel the puzzle it posed. It was found that the most important factor

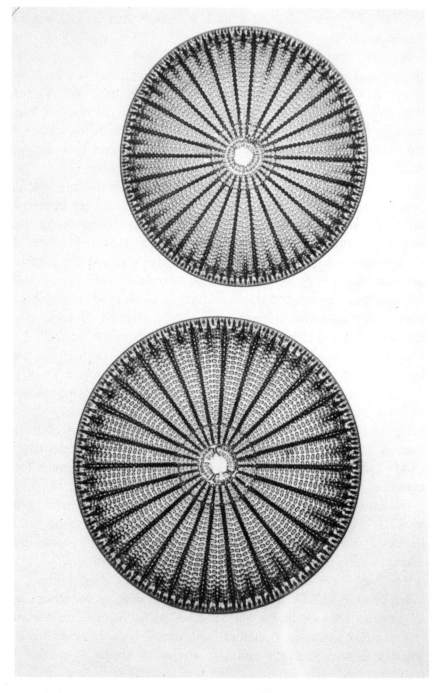

Two arachnoidiscus shells showing other fine markings in the glassy shell.
(100 ×)

affecting diatom growth was the amount of two chemicals available to them in the water. These chemicals are nitrates and phosphates. They are needed by diatoms for growth and reproduction. All other kinds of plants must get them also. What was it that caused the amounts of these substances to vary in the water?

In the winter, the water temperatures are low. Less light from the sun reaches the waters than at any other time. This means there are fewer diatoms. Since the plants are not using the nitrates and phosphates in the water, the amount of these chemicals increases. As the waters warm up and the sun's rays become stronger, the large accumulation of the two chemicals make the conditions ideal for the diatoms to flourish. This is what causes the big diatom population explosion in the spring.

By the summertime the numbers of diatoms are reduced in two ways. They are eaten by many kinds of animals, and also, they have used up most of the nitrates and phosphates available to them. By the fall, new phosphates and nitrates are brought to the surface from deeper waters by vertical currents. Large amounts of both chemicals are found on the ocean floor. This explains why the diatom population increases again even with cooler conditions and less light.

Diatoms have been on the earth for a long time, yet the individual diatom lives only a short time. Either it reproduces, or is eaten by some animal, or it dies. Large numbers of them are the main food for many small animals. Far more of them die. Their shells do not disappear, but slowly drift to the bottom. There they pile up slowly, over thousands and tens of thousands of years. In some places, this piling up continued for hundreds of thousands or even millions of years. If the remains of dead diatoms are not disturbed, the piles can form layers one thousand or more feet thick. The pressure of the waters above them presses them into relatively hard layers of rock.

In some parts of the world, the ocean floor was lifted above the surface while some other area was flooded. This was caused by movements of the crust of the earth and the uplifted areas became new land. In the United States, there are such rock layers— made up of diatoms shells of past ages—in Virginia and Maryland,

and there is one over 1400 feet thick in California. The number of shells in such layers is beyond counting.

The material mined from these layers is called diatomaceous earth. Imagine a little box one inch long, one inch wide, and one inch deep. If we filled it to the top it would contain one cubic inch of material. If the material filling the box is diatomaceous earth, it would contain about sixty million diatom shells. You can see why the amount in the mountains of the earth which were once sea bottom is beyond counting.

New deposits of diatom shells are being formed today on the bottoms of lakes, oceans, and seas. Big rivers such as the Nile, the Elbe, and the Amazon pour their waters into seas. The water they bring contains large numbers of diatoms which flourish in these seas.

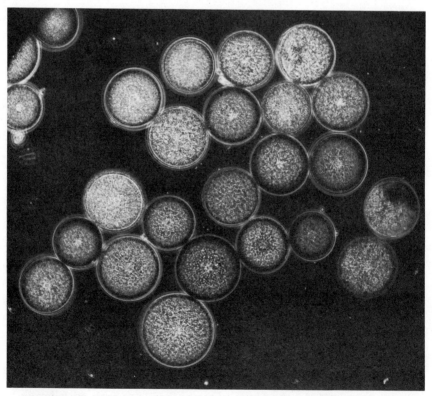

A small part of a drop of ocean water with twenty-five living coscinodiscus. The whole drop had many hundreds of the same type. (55 ×)

About one hundred years ago, many amateurs made slides of diatom shells to examine with a microscope. They put hundreds of shells on a single slide, arranging the shells in designs or in regular fashion for study. The slides are themselves objects of unusual beauty. Some slides even contained as many as a thousand different shells. It took days, weeks, and even months to make a single slide. No one seems to want to make these types of slides today. Many of those made long ago are still available. A single slide will give an interested person untold hours of pleasure. The photographs of some of the diatoms in this book were made from such slides.

Diatoms are useful plants. There is the role of the diatom as food producer in the oceans of the world. Also, the fossil diatom shells in diatomaceous earth are used as filters in a number of industries such as the dye and drug industries. The shells are so

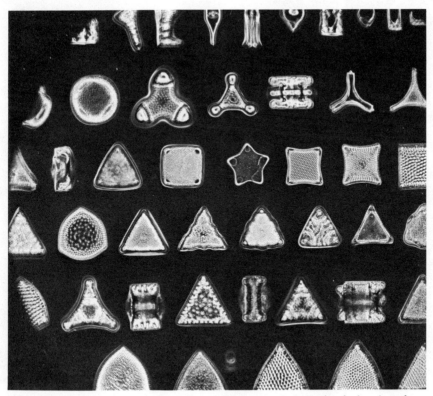

An arranged slide of fossil diatom shells from New Zealand showing the variety of shapes based on the triangle. (50 ×)

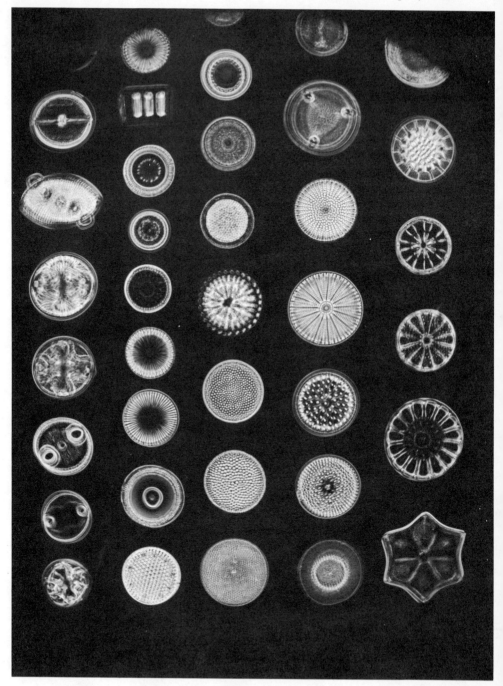

Variations of diatom shell structure with the circle as the basic design.
(75 ×)

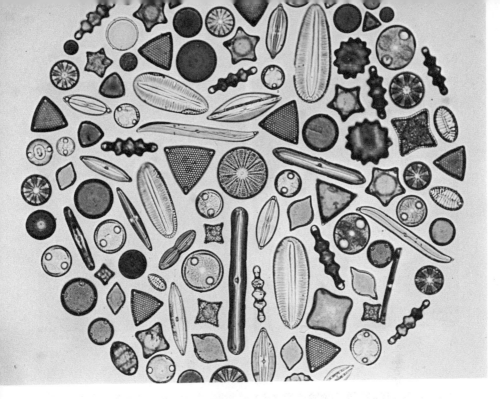

A

A. A circular arrangement of one hundred diatom shells. A slide such as this required untold hours to make since the individual shells are carefully selected and then placed on the slide, one by one (30 ×).

B. Part of the above slide (50 ×). Many such arranged slides have been made, often in other designs and sometimes with two hundred or more shells.

B

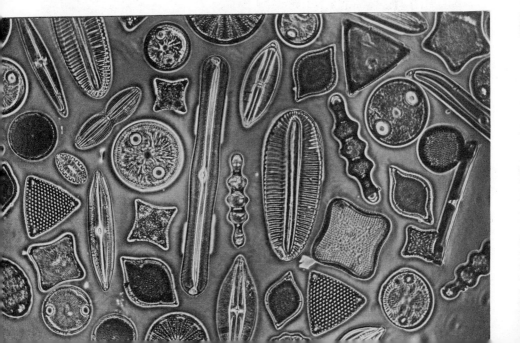

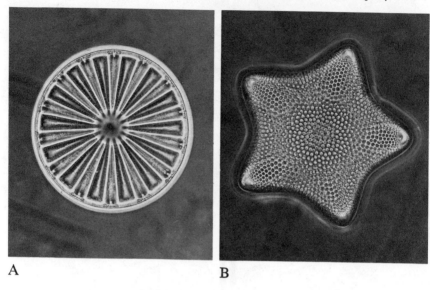

A   B

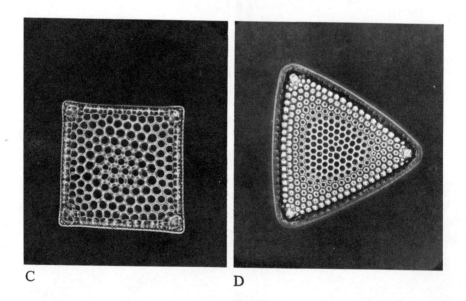

C   D

Four individual diatom shells photographed to show details of structure.
(150 ×)

A. A circular diatom.
B. A star-shaped shell.
C. A square-shaped shell.
D. A triangular shell.

tightly packed and are so fine that they will hold back small particles and allow only clear liquids to pass through.

Diatomaceous earth, along with some filler, is also used in making material to insulate homes and other buildings against heat and cold. The shells are hard enough to use in polishing many materials. Scouring powders, tooth paste, silver polish, and automobile polish all contain many diatom shells which make the polishes work.

This is quite a story for a tiny plant with a glassy covering. The diatoms are important. They are valuable. They are exquisitely beautiful. They are a challenge to the microscopist and the photographer.

Chapter 4

THE ALGAE—GRASS OF LAKES AND SEAS

The word "algae" refers to so many different kinds of plants that it is not always easy to decide just what it means. Most algae live in water; but not every water plant is an alga. Most algae are small, even microscopic in size; but every small plant is not an alga. What then, is an alga?

Algae are simple plants which are usually small and which usually live in water. They have simple methods of reproduction and generally simple life histories. Many of them consist of but a single cell. Diatoms are algae of this type.

Some algae are composed of so many cells, organized into bodies of definite form, that they are large and easy to see. Many of the brown and green seaweeds are very conspicuous; one brown alga sometimes reaches a length of over one hundred feet.

The one-celled and many-celled algae share one important quality. They all contain the green chemical chlorophyll and have the ability to manufacture food from simple chemicals.

Every collection of water will contain microscopic plants. These food factories of the sea are not always green. In addition to chlorophyll, they contain other colored substances which mask the green and give the plants a different appearance. Some of these are yellow, red, brown, and blue-green—a spectrum of attractive living plants.

The type of plants called blue-green algae are not always green or blue. This is one of the strange tricks that names play on us. Many of them are blue-green but the color of these simple plants depends on the materials in them. It ranges from yellow-green all the way to red. But they are alike in two ways. One is that the structure of the cell is the same in all the plants in this group. The second is the way these plants reproduce. Many of these algae are single cells. Some of them consist of colonies of cells which are attached and are all alike. Some are long and threadlike and consist of a number of cells, all alike, placed end to end.

The cell is a simple one. There seems to be no nucleus—which is unusual. There is another group of living things with cells without a nucleus. This group is the bacteria. Even without a nucleus they do have the chemical DNA which is found in the nuclei of all cells throughout the living world. In the blue-green algae and in the bacteria the DNA is scattered through the cell. The photograph of one blue-green alga, very much enlarged (over 700 times), shows the large number of dark grains throughout each cell which are made of DNA.

Only one method of reproduction has been found in this group of plants. This is by simple cell division. No joining of cells or other complex way of reproducing has ever been seen. In the division of the cell it seems as though the grains of DNA increase in number just before division and then are evenly divided between the two new cells.

All of these plants contain chlorophyll; the masking colored materials give these plants an attractive look. They are found in fresh and salt waters in all parts of the world.

The red sea looks red because there are so many blue-green algae of one type. It does not have a familiar name but its scientific name, *Trichodesmium erythraeum,* tells biologists something. The name *erythraeum* means "red." *Trichodesmium* means "hairlike chain of cells," which also describes how this plant looks.

Whenever one type of plant multiplies so rapidly that it gives the water its distinct color, the process is called "blooming." Blue-green algae very often bloom in all kinds of water. No one knows what causes the plants to bloom. One explanation is that the amount of

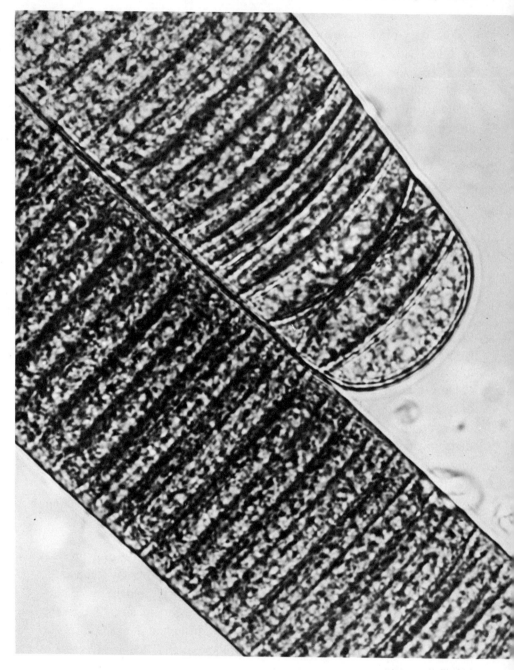

A particularly large species of the blue-green alga *Oscillatoria* (about 500 ×) from a small lake in New York City. It contains many granules of the hereditary material DNA.

some chemical which the plants need increases in an irregular way. Whenever this happens the plants grow very rapidly.

We may be unaware of what causes a bloom but we do know what the results of the bloom are. Usually it causes the water to smell and to taste bad. If this happens to water used for drinking, one of the big problems of the department of water supply is to get rid of the offending plants. This is done by adding a chemical containing copper, which is known to kill algae. The small amount of the chemical needed to destroy the plants has no effect on man or other animals.

If you have an aquarium at home in which you are keeping some small fish it will turn green if you allow it to get too much light. Some algae in the water have bloomed. You can correct this by moving the tank away from the light and by adding a copper penny to the water. Enough copper will dissolve to kill the algae.

One of the most common of the blue-green algae is one called *Oscillatoria*. It grows in large mats on the shallow floor of lakes and ponds. The plant consists of long threads with narrow cells attached end to end. When we look at this plant under a microscope, the threads slowly move back and forth; they oscillate. This behavior gave the plant its name. The mats are deep blue-green in color. In one small lake in the heart of New York City it grows so richly that it covers hundreds of square yards of the shallow lake bottom near its margins. Often, clumps separate from the bottom and float on the surface.

Some blue-green algae have another unusual ability. They are found at the margins of hot springs in many parts of the world. The temperatures run as high as 140 degrees Fahrenheit. This temperature would kill most living things, but it seems to have no effect on the algae.

The chemical chlorophyll in another group of algae—the green algae—is not a single chemical molecule; it is a mixture of at least four different molecules. Two of them are green—chlorophyll A and chlorophyll B. An orange chemical called carotene is also part of the mixture. This is the substance which gives carrots, oranges, and sweet potatoes their color. The fourth chemical is a yellow one called xanthophyll. This is the part of the plant along with carotene which gives butter its color.

The green algae are found in all kinds of water and a few of them live on land.

Spirogyra, a common green alga, is found in ponds, lakes, ditches, swamps, and often in slow-moving streams. It is a one-celled plant but it grows in long threads of cells attached end to end. Usually it grows in such large masses of these tangled threads that they float at the surface. The cells are held together by a slippery covering. It is easy to recognize *Spirogyra* without using a microscope. It is slippery to touch—the only common alga with this quality. The long threads of this plant never branch, as do some related ones.

Each cell of the plant is constructed like a long tube. The chlorophyll is contained in a long ribbon, coiled just inside the wall in a spiral running from one end of the cell to the other. In

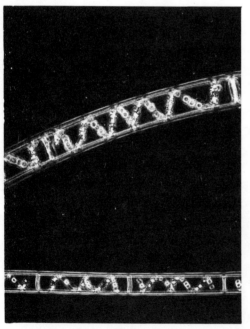 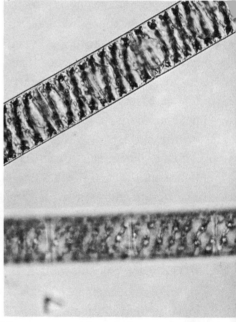

A. Two different species of the fresh-water green alga, *Spirogyra.* Both of these species have a single spiral band of chlorophyll. The main difference between the two species is the size of the cells. (40 ×)
B. A species of *Spirogyra* with several bands of chlorophyll. (40 ×)

some kinds of *Spirogyra* there are two or three such bands tightly packed in the cell. Each *Spirogyra* cell has a single nucleus. It takes careful looking to see it, but it is visible in the living cell.

Spirogyra reproduces by simple cell division. Since the two cells formed are attached to one another and this continues with more and more cells produced, a thread of cells is formed. If the thread breaks at any point, two threads are formed which can then grow as new cells are added. This is the usual method of producing new plants.

Sometimes *Spirogyra* will show threads of cells reproducing in another way. Two threads will lie side by side. Each cell in each thread grows a bump. The growth continues until they join. At this time the two threads are connected by a series of tubes and the plants look like a ladder with many rungs.

The cell material in one cell begins to move slowly through the tube into the adjoining cell. This happens all along the ladder. The two nuclei join. This is a sexual process, one of the simpler ways in which sexual reproduction happens. The new nucleus formed by the two that joined forms a thick wall. Later, when conditions are just right, it will begin to divide and produce new filaments.

Spirogyra has been used to perform experiments designed to study the process of food manufacture. Leeuwenhoek saw this plant and was the first to describe it.

The green algae are easy to photograph—they stand still for their pictures.

Every one of us is attracted by symmetry. The world of microscopic living things is often a symmetrical world. The desmids, one-celled green plants, are among the very attractive symmetrical living things. There are at least two thousand known varieties and they offer us an unusual display of structure.

The desmids are found only in clear, fresh waters. When there is much decay in the water, they do not survive. We find them mostly on the bottom in large numbers of clean lakes and ponds where the water is slightly acid.

Each plant is a single cell, although some do form colonies of similar cells. Each cell consists of two equal halves which are joined in the middle. In some, only the insides of the cells are seen to be symmetrical. In others, the outer wall and the inside are pinched

Two threads of *Spirogyra* with a connecting bridge built during the reproductive process in which nuclei from two cells combine. One combined cell is visible. This one will produce a new thread of many cells arranged end to end by repeated cell divisions. (100 ×)

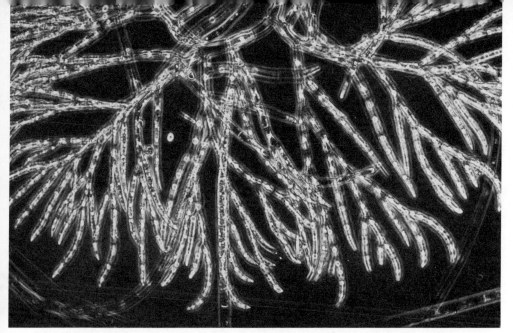

Branching threads of a grass-green alga called *Cladophora*. When this one was collected it was a small, pale green, gelatinous structure about the size of a rice grain. I pressed it between two glass slides and the structure of the alga as seen in this photograph was revealed. (50 ×)

The water net, a grass-green alga whose cells form the attractive structure you see here. (50 ×)

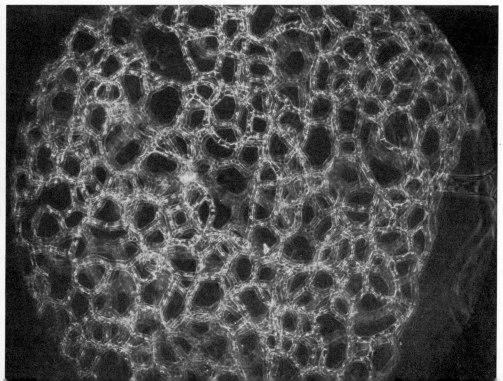

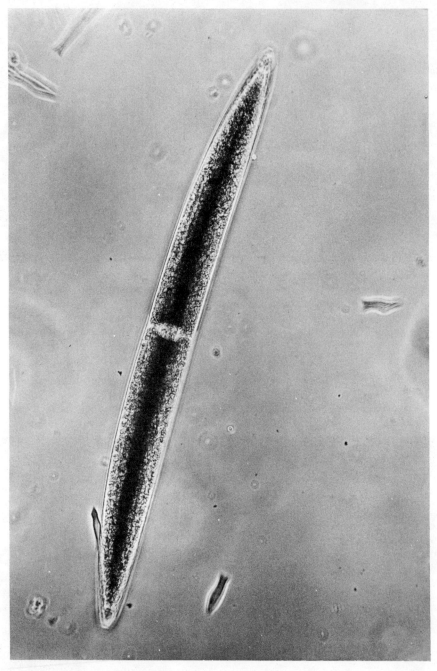

The desmid, *Closterium,* a common green plant in fresh water. It is a symmetrical plant in which the shape varies from crescent moon shape to the above. (50 ×)

in two with a bridge of living substance connecting the halves. In all of them the color is emerald green. They are small plants but they are unusually attractive.

Closterium is one of the most common ones. Some types look like a green crescent moon. The nucleus is found in the connecting bridge.

Each half of the cell has a large green body filling most of the cell. There are two clear bubbles, one at each end, filled with water. They also contain tiny crystals of a chemical called gypsum. When we magnify these bubbles 400 or more times the crystals are seen to dance actively and never to stop. As long as the cell is alive the particles bounce around.

What is it that makes them move? There is nothing that we can see that seems to explain what is going on. We now know that the force that moves the crystals is the constant movement of the water molecules. The moving molecules of water have enough energy to move the larger gypsum molecules whenever they collide.

When *Closterium* has grown to its full size it reproduces by cell division. This sometimes takes a day or more to complete. The two halves of the cell separate and each half grows another half. There are now two plants where there was one. Each of the new plants then grows until it reaches full size and the process happens all over again.

Some plants in the desmid group also reproduce by a sexual process. When this happens the living material of two different cells flows out of the cell walls and fuses to form a single cell. This single cell then produces the new plant. Most of the details of how this happens are not known. They await the skill and desire of some questioning person to find out.

Pediastrum is still another of the many kinds of algae. It is a plant which consists of a number of cells arranged in a small flat plate. There are different varieties and they may have as few as 8 cells or as many as 128.

The plant floats around near the surface of quiet bodies of fresh water. It is a very small plant and sometimes it can be passed by when a drop of water is being examined. It is worth searching for.

Reproduction is different from any other method so far described. Each cell in the colony has a single nucleus. If the cell is separated

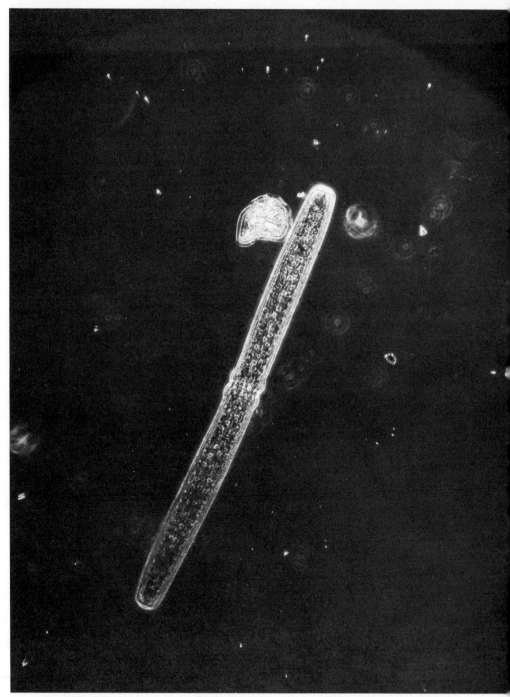

Another species of desmid (*Pleurotaenium*) from the same water as yielded *Closterium*. (50 ×)

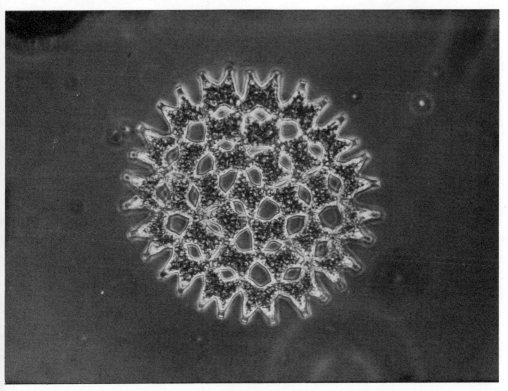

A species of *Pediastrum*—an attractive fresh-water alga. *Pediastrum* is quite small and is easily overlooked. (200 ×)

from the others in the colony it could live alone. Each cell goes through a number of divisions of its nucleus, and each of the nuclei formed—with a little of the surrounding living material—produces a cell with two flagella. These cells swim around within the cell boundary. Then they swim out of the cell through a tiny opening.

When they escape the parent cell they are all contained in a sac. They swim about for a time, then slow down and arrange themselves in the form of the original colony. The cells lose their whips and take on the shape of the cell that formed them. Next the membrane disappears and a new colony exists. Each cell in the colony can give rise to a new colony—a very efficient way of producing new plants.

There is no more thrilling sight than the view through the microscope of a colony of *Volvox* rolling gently and slowly through its drop of water. It is a ball of cells about half the size of the head of a pin, and can be seen without a microscope.

The ball consists of one layer of cells. Each of the cells has two short whips or flagella. The color of the colony is a soft grass-green, and when there are large numbers of colonies they color the water green.

Volvox is found in fresh water all over the world. Sometimes it blooms, as so many other algae do. One June day I was collecting in a productive pond which looked greener than usual—like pea soup. My hand lens revealed that there were millions of colonies of volvox in the water. The viewing was good for a long time.

Leeuwenhoek was the first to see and describe *Volvox*. This he did in a letter written early in the year 1700. His words may sound a little strange but we do get a clear picture of what he was describing. "I collected some water from some ditches and Canals on the 30th of August: and when I reached home, I examined it. While I was busy looking at the many kinds of animals a-swimming in it, I saw floating in it and seeming to move by themselves, a great many green round particles of the bigness of sand grains.

"When I put these little bodies before my microscope, I saw that they were not just round, but that their margins showed many little projecting particles . . . and it looked to me in the whole circumference of the little ball, eighty such particles were set, all arranged in an orderly way and at equal distances from one another, so that there were a very large number of these projecting particles.

"Each of these little bodies had enclosed within it five, six, seven, nay, some even twelve very little round globules, in structure like the body itself wherein they were contained."

What a remarkably accurate description! When we think how simple were the microscopes Leeuwenhoek used, we cannot help realizing how unusual were his powers of observation and his inclination to report only what he saw. It is so easy when looking at new and strange things with a microscope to imagine that we see many things which are not really there. Leeuwenhoek rarely did this.

There are many species of *Volvox,* including some with five hundred to a thousand cells—all almost exactly alike—to some with more than twenty thousand cells. The cells of each colony

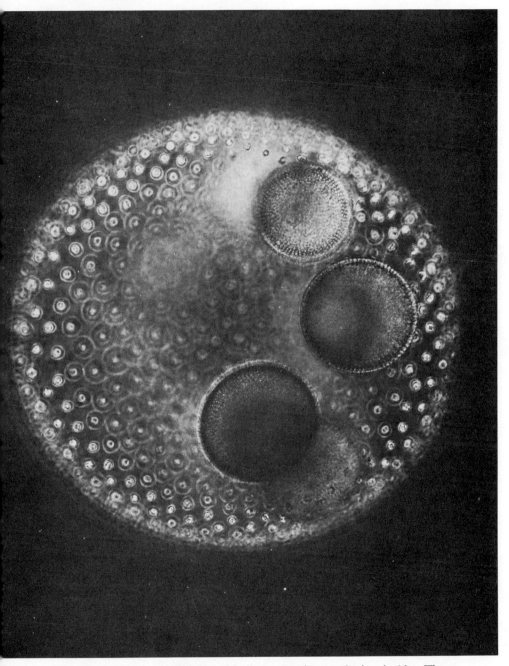

A mother colony of *Volvox* with four daughter colonies inside. The individual cells can be seen in the parent colony. Since the colony is a ball of cells, the cells are not all visible in the photograph. *Volvox* is beautiful to watch as it rolls slowly and gracefully by. (75 ×)

form a hollow ball with one layer of cells. Each cell contains chlorophyll and has two short flagella. The cells seem to be enclosed in a kind of clear jelly and they are connected with each other.

Volvox reproduces in two ways. In one, groups of cells pinch off inside the ball and they form smaller daughter colonies. The smaller daughter colonies are clearly seen inside the larger parent colony. This is what Leeuwenhoek was describing in the "five, six, seven, nay, some even twelve very little globules, in structure like the body itself wherein they were contained." Only a few cells of the parent colony are able to form daughter colonies. These are a bit larger than the other cells in the colony.

Before the daughter colonies are ready to live on their own, each one turns inside out. After this happens, the parent colony dies and breaks up. This frees the new colonies to live on their own.

Volvox also reproduces sexually. Some cells in the colony become very large. They give rise to egg cells. Others produce small sacs of long, thin cells each with two flagella. These are the male sex cells. One of these male cells must combine with an egg to form a new *Volvox* colony. When the two cells join they do not form the new plant at once. The combined cell forms a thick covering and when conditions are good the single cell escapes from its wall and swims away. It divides and redivides to form a ball of cells. This ball must also turn inside out before it is finished with the job of developing.

One day in late spring a small pond in eastern Long Island looked to me to be strangely clear and yellow. The pond had been a source of many wonderful days of looking through the microscope. It had never looked like this before. What was happening? I collected some of the water and took it home to explore with the microscope.

When I examined the water I found that in it there was one kind of living thing, and one only. It was one species of dinoflagellate—one which bore the name *Ceratium*.

What are dinoflagellates and how can we know when we are looking at one? The name *dinoflagellate* sounds very much like the name dinosaur. You know that the name *dinosaur* means "terrible lizard." What is so terrible about these tiny microscopic plants? The prefix *dino* in dinoflagellate was not formed from the same prefix

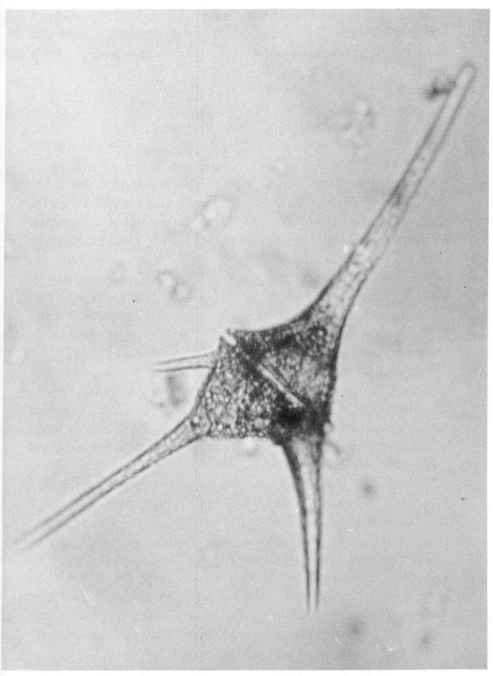

A fresh-water species of the dinoflagellate *Ceratium* which bloomed in a small pond one spring day. Compare it with the common marine species in the next photograph. (400 ×)

in Greek that was used to coin the name dinosaur. The *dino* comes from a different word meaning "whirling," not "terrible." When you look at these plants moving around you see why they were given this name.

Dinoflagellate cells have two flagella. These move the plant in a whirling path through the water, so the name is descriptive of the swimming behavior. The dinoflagellates are very important creatures in the plankton of salt waters. Here they are found in fantastically large numbers. Some, as *Ceratium,* also live in fresh water.

In one of my frequent visits to the shore I scrambled out to the end of a rock jetty where a swift current brought a rich supply of plankton. My collecting net seined out of the fast-moving waters enough organisms to color the water yellow. My hand lens told the story.

The tube was filled with tens of thousands of a species of *Ceratium* along with many other kinds of plants and animals. Two other kinds of dinoflagellate were also collected. These move faster than *Ceratium* but I was able to get photographs of all three when I got back to my microscope.

Most dinoflagellates are made up of a single cell with just one nucleus. The boundary of the cell has grooves in which the flagella are attached. One groove circles the cell near the middle. The other points toward the back end of the cell. One of the flagella is found in the encircling groove. The other ones trails toward the back and is the one used in movement.

Some of the dinoflagellates have the outer wall covered with tiny plates which make them look scaly. They have chlorophyll but it is usually masked by other colored pigments, which explains the color of waters in which they are growing.

The chlorophyll means, of course, that these creatures make their own food. Dinoflagellates do best when phosphates and nitrates have been largely removed from the water by the rapid growth of diatoms. The numbers of dinoflagellates are greatest after diatoms have bloomed. The dinoflagellates are also an important food source in the ocean, but not as important as the diatoms.

Once in a while some species of dinoflagellates increase in numbers in some waters for reasons not yet understood. This happened in 1948 off the coast of Florida, when one kind of dinoflagellate

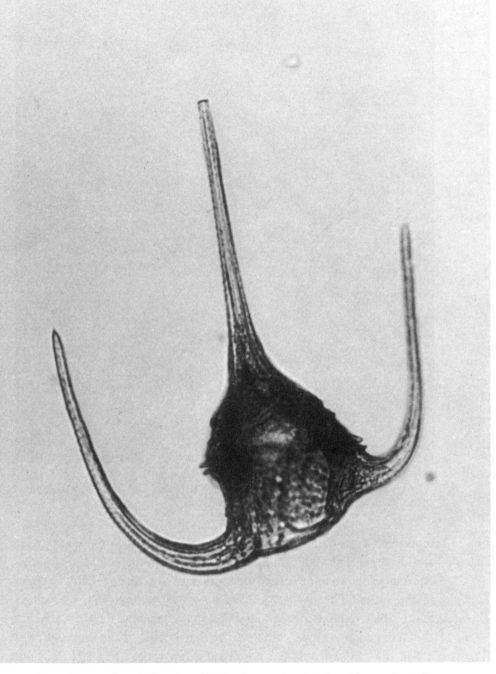

A marine species of *Ceratium*. In the late spring it often blooms in such numbers that it fills collecting containers. (400 ×)

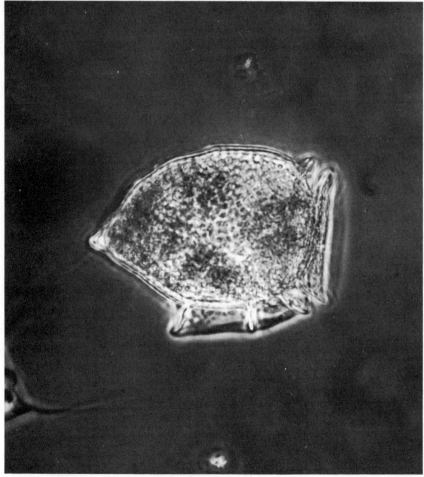

Another species of marine dinoflagellate, *Dinophysis*. Only a few of these have appeared in my collections although it is reported as fairly common. The scaly outer covering can be seen. (400 ×)

multiplied so fast that there were countless trillions in the water, over a wide area. This large number gave off quantities of some poisonous materials and they also used up much of the available oxygen in the water. The result was that over fifty million fish, as well as many other animals, were killed. So many were washed ashore that they created a serious threat to human health. This outbreak was called the "red tide." It has happened a few times since 1948 but not with such violent effects.

Some dinoflagellates are phosphorescent. At night when no other

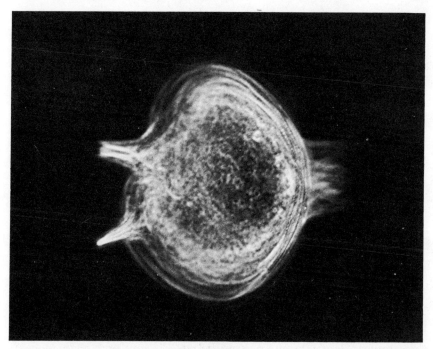

The delicately pink dinoflagellate, *Peridinium*. It moves ceaselessly. This one moved just as I exposed the film. (400 ×)

light is shining they glow when disturbed. One species in the tropics is a large plant, for a one-celled organism, and is found in large numbers. When they are disturbed they give off a spectacular light. The name of this plant is *Noctiluca*. This name means "night light," an appropriate one in view of its behavior.

Chapter 5

ARCHITECTS OF THE MICROSCOPIC WORLD

The study of microscopic life leads down many paths and byways. Following any one will bring rewards. Every living thing, even the simplest, is a vibrant, pulsing being. Finding one, then identifying it, is only the first step in learning about it. How is it equipped to survive? What is its life history? What is its place in the larger environment in which it is found? The answers to these questions and others are not always known. There is more required than just viewing with the microscope to find answers.

Realizing this was what sent me to the ocean to explore the infinitely great riches of life which it contains. The surface of the earth is 70 to 75 per cent water. All but a small part of this is salt water. These waters teem with life both large and small. The largest animals which have ever lived, the sulfur-bottom whales, are marine animals. Countless varieties of animals and plants also abound in the salt waters of oceans, seas, and bays.

There is another advantage in working with marine plankton; that is, they are available all through the year. The types of organisms change through the seasons, but some living forms can be found no matter what the weather is.

I have had the good fortune in recent years of living within a hundred yards of the Atlantic Ocean and just five minutes away from the waters of Jamaica Bay. Not only am I able to sample and collect the riches of these two bodies of water, I can begin to study them and to photograph the living organisms immediately, when they are most active.

The two collecting sites from which I have made regular samplings proved to be so productive that it was not necessary to look anywhere else. A stone jetty juts out into the Atlantic waters as they enter the East Rockaway inlet between the Rockaway and Long Beach peninsulas. A strong current moves swiftly by the end of the rocks and brings with it a never-ending supply of plankton organisms. Dipping the net so that it faces the current sweeps all kinds of animals and plants into the tube.

The Rockaway Coast Guard station on the bay side of the Rockaway peninsula is an equally reliable source of supply. Slower currents, sometimes aided by the frequent movements of Coast Guard cutters into and out of their harbor, add their energy to the currents and help bring a supply of plankton. The officer of the day willingly permits collection.

Two very interesting types of protozoa which are exclusively marine are the Foraminifera and Radiolaria. I had never looked at living members of these types until I collected some from the East Rockaway inlet. Both are related to *Ameba* and *Actinosphaerium* and have pseudopods which suggest this relationship.

For some time I used slides of the beautifully sculptured shells of these interesting animal architects to observe and photograph. The photographs included here are of fossil types which have a special importance. The photographs of living ones brought great satisfaction.

Life has been on the earth at least a billion years and possibly as long as two or even three billion years. There is much evidence that this is so. We are not sure, however, about what the earliest and simplest life on earth was. We do know that it was much simpler than the tiny animals that so fascinated Antony van Leeuwenhoek.

Once living things were on the earth, new varieties and new types somehow began to appear. If there are well over a million different kinds of animals living on the earth today, there must be some way of explaining how they came to be. Two facts provide some clues to the long history of life on the earth and the many changes that occurred in times past. One is that living things have the ability to produce new living things very much like themselves. We know now that there is a material that the parent generation passes on to each of its offspring. You have probably heard it called a gene. It is the substance of inheritance throughout the living world.

The chemical substances in the nucleus of all cells of every kind of living thing include one with the name DNA. DNA is a kind of blueprint. It carries in its complicated molecules some information. The information is a type of code. Cat DNA contains the blueprint for producing a cat and *not* a tiger or a dog or a beetle. Dog DNA contains the complete blueprint for making a dog and not any other kind of living thing. Human DNA includes the information for producing only a new human being.

No two living things are exactly alike. Although we have no problem in seeing that a group of kittens are all kittens and that they will grow up to become cats, they will differ from one another. They will have different-colored fur. They will differ in many ways. Each one will be an individual, with its own special qualities. They have inherited a blueprint for producing a particular kind of living thing, a kitten. The blueprint also includes information for producing differences between individuals of the same type.

DNA molecules have one important property, in addition to containing a blueprint. They sometimes change spontaneously. When this happens, the new generation will have one or more differences in traits. These are then passed along by inheritance to new generations. These changes in DNA which can be inherited are called *mutations.* This, we think, is one of the ways that new kinds of living things have appeared over the millions of years in which these changes have taken place.

A foraminiferan is a protozoan. It is an animal made up of a single cell. It is unusual in its ability to build a shell of chalk which encloses the living animal. All the living types are found in the salt water of seas, bays, and parts of the ocean rather close to the shore. They are more plentiful in warm waters. Finally, they are bottom dwellers, crawling along the soft floor in their search for food.

There is a layer of soft mud, called ooze, on the shallow floor of

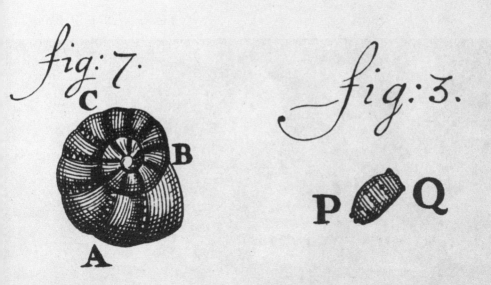

TWO OF LEEUWENHOEK'S FIGURES ILLUSTRATING LETTERS 125 AND 144
enlarged from the original engravings.

Fig. 7, ABC.—Shell of a Foraminiferan (*Polystomella* ?).
Fig. 3, PQ.—The Ciliate *Coleps*. (The original measures only 6 mm. in length.)

A drawing of a foraminiferan shell drawn by Leeuwenhoek. It is probably the same species as one shown in the next two photos. Which one does it resemble?

the ocean close to the continents. Most of this ooze is made up of the shells of dead foraminifera.

Foraminifera have been on the earth for a long time. There is some evidence that they flourished in salt waters a half-billion years ago. This we know because the shells are hard enough to be preserved as fossils. Most of the foraminifera of times past, as well as those alive today, are small animals. They must be examined with a microscope to see details of their structure. There are many which are as much as an inch or more across.

Once they were on the earth, they flourished. They multiplied so fast in many parts of the world that their shells make up more than half of the floor of all deep seas covering the earth—over fifty million square miles of it. Think of how many individual animals must have lived in the past to leave shells which slowly piled up

A photograph of twelve foraminiferan shells. The lighting used in making this one was different from the light used in photographing the same shells for the next photo. Each type of lighting brings out different structural details. (50 ×)

until they formed layers thousands upon thousands of feet thick. The chalk cliffs of Dover, on the English Channel, were formed in this fashion. They were lifted out of the sea ages ago and now stand high above the waters of the channel. These cliffs are composed almost entirely of foraminiferan shells.

There are large areas of thick limestone in Asia, in the Alps in Europe, and in other parts of the earth. This limestone was formed from the same kinds of shells. The center of the city of Paris is built on limestone of the same origin and many of the buildings of Paris are made of this limestone. A hand lens magnifying from 10 to 15 times will show the shells in the walls of many such buildings.

The great pyramids of Egypt are constructed of limestone built by the shells of one type of foram. The white beaches of many tropical shores are covered with sand which is almost entirely made up of the same kinds of shells. One gram of ocean beach sand (this is a small part of an ounce) contains about fifty thousand of these shells.

The foraminifera have lived continuously on the earth for an enormously long time. For this reason they can be used in learning something about the history of the earth and its life.

Oil is often found near layers of rock containing foraminifera. When oil wells are drilled, the core of the drilling operation is brought to the surface. Some of these cores are taken from layers thousands of feet below the surface. The drilling somehow leaves most of the foraminiferal shells complete and undamaged, and it is possible to use the shells of fossil types to date the layers of rock. Rocks found in different parts of the earth often contain the same types of shells. This suggests that the layers of rock in different

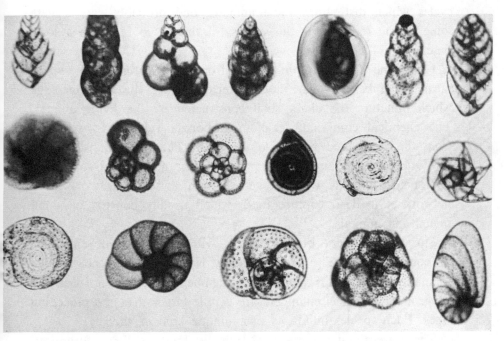

This photograph was made with what is called normal bright light illumination. It pictures the same twelve shells of lime as are shown in the preceding photo. (50 ×)

places are about the same age. It is also possible to deduce the kind of conditions that existed when these animals were alive.

In the ancient past, two kinds of changes were altering the surface of the earth itself. Land areas were being worn away slowly but surely by many forces. The crust of the earth shifted and heaved from time to time in response to forces operating deep in the earth.

New land areas were lifted out of the seas while the waters displaced by these movements covered sections of land which were destined to remain covered for a long time. The face of the earth was changing.

At the same time animal and plant life was also changing. New types of organisms appeared while many of the old disappeared. The changing earth challenged the plants and animals. Those which adapted, survived; those which were not equipped to do so, perished.

The foraminifera did not change much over these long periods of time. They were adapted to their environment and survived, so from them we can learn the ways of life as well as the life cycles which distinguish these animals, and probably can suggest some of the reasons for the success of the group for such a long time.

The name *foraminiferan* comes from two Latin words which mean "hole bearer." The holes referred to are the tiny openings which puncture the chalk shell constructed by the living animal. The chemical compound calcium carbonate (chalk) is extracted from the water and built into the shell. The living substance of the foram streams out of the openings in branching and sometimes unbranched threads which together form a sticky network. The network is used to capture food, which usually consists of small plants and animals.

Most foraminifera produce shells with a number of chambers or compartments. The original cavity is the smallest one. As the animal grows it adds connecting chambers, often in a spiral arrangement. The new chambers are a little larger than the preceding ones. Each species builds its own unique kind of shell.

There are about ten thousand different kinds of living foraminifera. In this large group there are many kinds of life histories.

For example, there may be two distinct generations. They can be

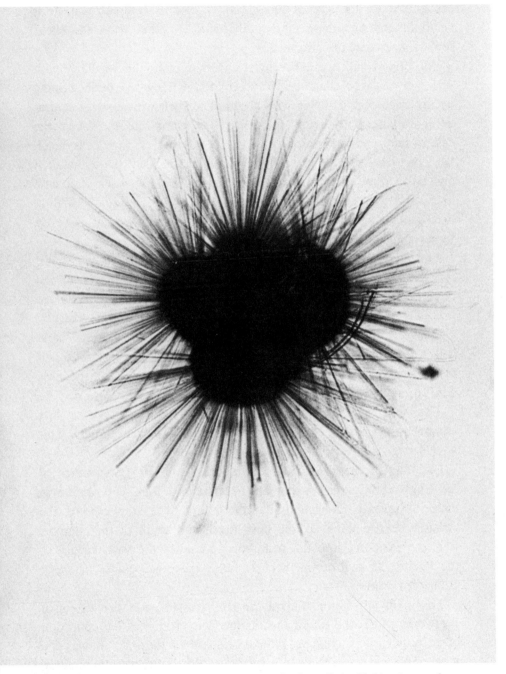

The first live foraminiferan I ever saw. It is called *Globigerina* and is very common in the ocean waters. I was not able to show details of structure but the many pseudopods are shown. (300 ×)

recognized by the size of the initial or central compartment. It is small in one and large in the other. In all other ways the shells look alike when fully formed.

An animal with a small central chamber alternates regularly with one with a large chamber. We can follow the cycle by beginning at any stage. Let us begin with a complete shell with a small central compartment. The living substance has many nuclei. When the cell is ready to reproduce, it forms a number of tiny cells, each with one nucleus. All the cells look the same. They leave the shell and swim away. Each one then builds the first chamber of a new individual. The animal within feeds and grows, gradually adding new compartments as it outgrows the older ones. Soon it is ready to reproduce.

The living material divides into a number of cells of two types. Some develop flagella—they are able to swim. The other type of cell is ameba-like, moving slowly with its pseudopods. These cells are sex cells.

One cell of each type must meet and combine to form a single cell. Large numbers of both types of cell are shed into the water and meet by chance. The fused cells become the first cell of the next generation.

The next step in development is the production of the first chamber—a small one. It grows and produces new chambers. This is the stage with which we began the story.

One day in the year 1872 the wooden ship H.M.S. *Challenger* left England on a journey that was to last almost four years and cover close to seventy thousand miles of sailing. The ship crossed the Atlantic several times, sailing both north and south of the equator. It also went down into the Antarctic and sailed the vast reaches of the Pacific, as well as many bays, seas, and other bodies of water connected with it.

The main job of the staff of the ship was to chart the waters of the world. A second major task assigned to them was the collection of as much information as possible on life in the seas. It was the most important and successful expedition of its kind ever undertaken. In the course of four years, over four thousand new species of animals were discovered, collected, and described. Specimens of

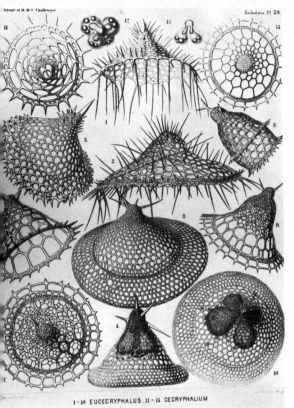

1 - 10 EUCECRYPHALUS . 11 - 14 CECRYPHALIUM

Two of the many plates of *Radiolaria* shells drawn by Ernst Haeckel from specimens collected by H.M.S. *Challenger* in its famous voyage.

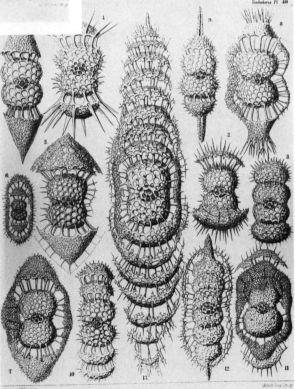

1-3 PANARTUS . 4 PANARTIDIUM . 5-8 PERIPANARTUS .
9 PANARIUM . 10 OMMATOCAMPE . 11-13 ZYGARTUS

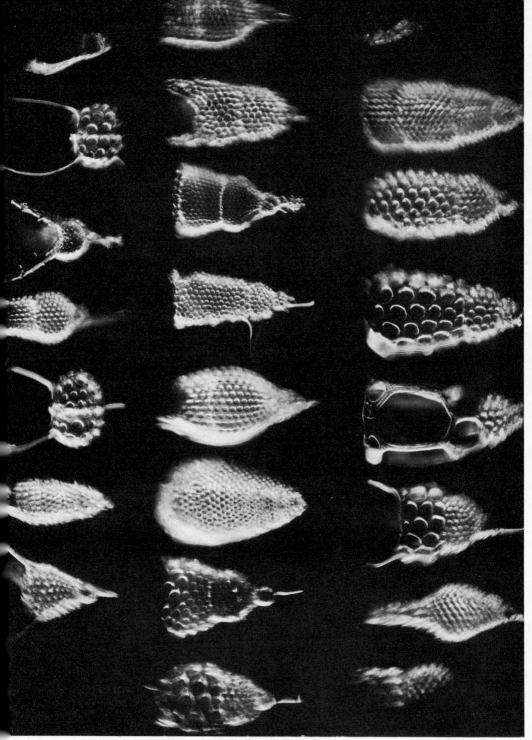

Photograph of a number of fossil *Radiolaria* shells from Barbados in the British West Indies. Compare the structure with the next photo, in which bright field illumination is used. (50 ×)

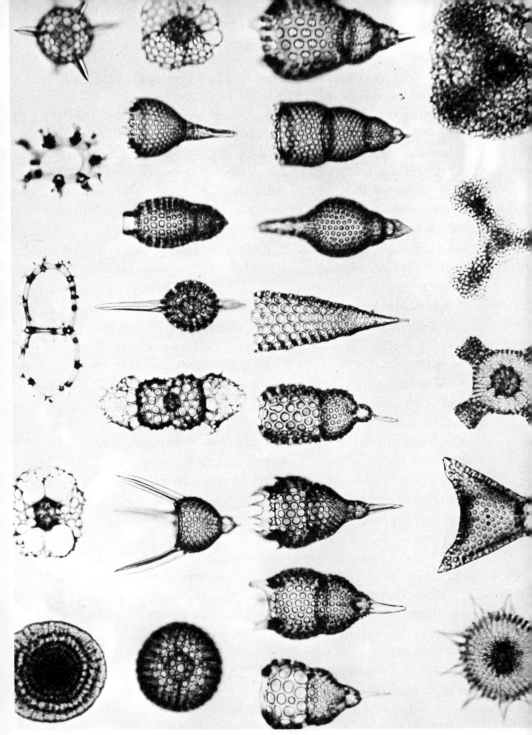

A different group of *Radiolaria* shells from the same slide as was used in making the previous photo. The slide has one hundred shells in all. (50 ×)

all kinds of animals were preserved. They were either sent back to England or brought back when the ship returned.

Experts on different types of animals were invited to study the collections and to describe the results of this remarkable journey. The scientific results of the trip were reported in fifty large volumes; forty of these books describe a number of groups of animals. The best known of these reports fill three huge books.

These were written by Ernst Haeckel, one of the great biologists of the nineteenth century. All three books were devoted to a group of microscopic animals called Radiolaria. Haeckel drew more than half of the more than one thousand beautiful drawings which illustrate these volumes.

Radiolaria are beautiful protozoa. Their skeletons are made of the same chemical, silicon, which diatoms use to build their unusual-looking shells. The living radiolarian builds a skeleton of needles of silicon fused into networks of great beauty and symmetry.

Radiolarians are found in all the seas of the world, in all climates, and at all depths. The majority of these delicate animals live in the surface waters where they float freely. They differ in this way from the foraminifera, which are largely bottom-dwellers. Radiolarians are most abundant in warm waters, especially in the Pacific Ocean, which has a rich population of these animals. There are none found in fresh water.

When the animals die, their shells slowly sink to the bottom where they pile up in thick layers. These layers are called radiolarial ooze. It is usually found at depths of from 12,000 to 18,000 feet below the ocean's surface. The chemical silicon is able to resist the pressures at these depths. The skeletons of the radiolarians are in good condition either in the ooze or in layers of rock formed from skeletons of animals that lived in the distant past.

Fossil radiolarians have been found in rocks that were formed more than 500,000,000 years ago. Most of the fossil types are less than 200,000,000 years old, and are found in a number of very hard rock layers in many parts of the world.

The body of the radiolarian consists of one single cell even though it looks more complicated. The cell has two main parts separated by a membrane with many small holes or a few large

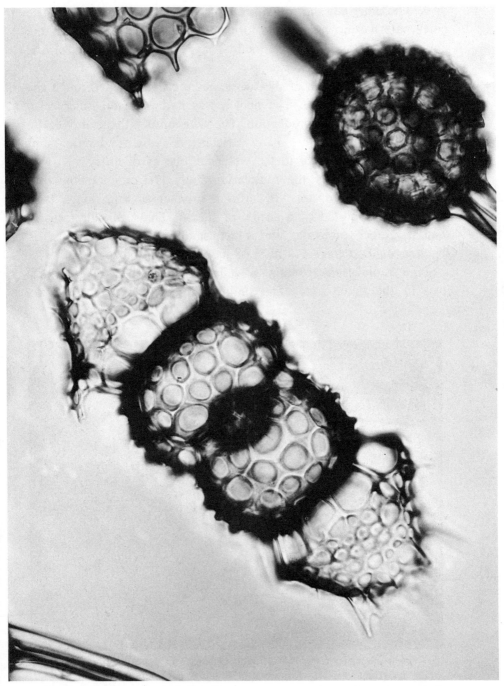

A single radiolarian shell photograph on two levels to show the central capsule as well as the outer shell. (300 ×)

ones. The inner capsule contains one or more than one nucleus. The outer part has no nucleus. It forms the "false feet" by which the animal moves and captures food. They, too, are relatives of the foraminifera and of *Ameba*.

The living substance of the two zones are connected through the holes in the membrane. The nucleus, as it does in all other cells, controls growth and reproduction. The skeleton is a thing of delicate, lacelike beauty. There are many varieties; as many as four thousand different types are alive in the waters of the earth today.

The outer zone of the radiolarian body is frothy-looking with bubbles of different sizes. It forms a number of thin, long "false feet," each supported by a needle of silicon. These animals feed on diatoms, other protozoa, and other small animals. The food is digested in food bubbles—as it is in all other protozoa.

Some radiolarians contain a yellowish one-celled plant which lives in the outer zone. The radiolarian and the plant seem to

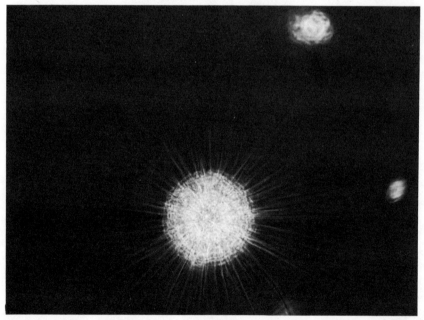

A living radiolarian from the Atlantic Ocean. The delicate, long pseudopods and their slender, firm supports stand out. The frothy mass of living substance is also clearly shown. The living animal is pinkish-red in color. (200 ×)

help one another. Many radiolarians, especially those which live in warm water, are phosphorescent. When they are disturbed at night by a boat moving through the water, they light up areas of the sea.

Not too much is known about the life cycle of these animals. One method of reproduction has been seen. The nuclei in the central section divide very rapidly. They form many smaller nuclei. Each nucleus, surrounded by a little of the living substance, forms a long flagellum. The capsule separates from the skeleton and drifts down to a depth of 500 to 600 feet. Here the membrane breaks apart and the cells are released to swim around. Each one is able to build the typical silicon skeleton and grows into a complete new individual.

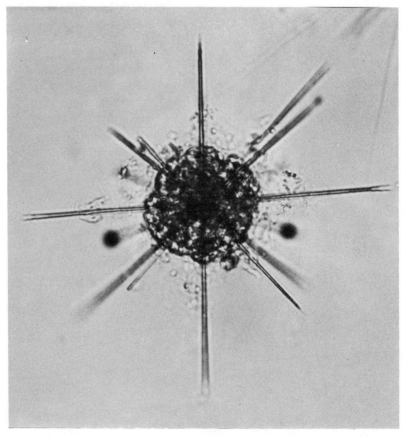

Another living species of living radiolarian. This one has fewer pseudopods than the previous one but its frothy living material is clearly seen. (200 ×)

It does seem strange that a kind of animal life with so many thousands of species and a history on the earth going back at least a half-billion years should be studied so little. Now that scientists all over the world have become more interested in the living things in the ocean, maybe enough will be done, enough problems will be solved, to give us a more complete story of the wonderful-looking animals.

Chapter 6

WATER FLEAS AND OTHER ONE-EYED GIANTS OF THE DROP

The pond was especially quiet one day early in June. The water looked clear and it did not seem that much life stirred below the still surface. I moved close to the edge of the pond. In the shade of a red maple tree, a frog dived below the surface and out of sight at my approach. Streamers of mud in the water showed me where the frog had disappeared.

I looked carefully and began to notice more signs of life. Dragonflies skimmed close to the surface and now and then dipped the back ends of their bodies into the water. With each dip they deposited an egg in the water. The eggs would develop into water animals. Not until the following spring would the new generation of dragonflies leave the waters of the pond and take to the air.

Slender water striders moved easily over the surface. Each of the six legs dimpled the skin formed by the top layer of molecules of the water but did not break through. The weight of the animals was miraculously supported. A quiet buzzing and humming told me of the presence of more small animals which could be seen if I took the pains.

But I was in search of smaller prey. Was there more life below the surface of the pond? Some sweeps through the water, a few feet from the shore with a collecting net, gave me my answer. A dozen sweeps through the water gathered most of the living things in a gallon or more of water.

The collecting bottle was a fascinating sight. It boiled with life. Many kinds of creatures moved aimlessly—or so it seemed. Some of them were very small and could be seen only as moving, tiny specks. Some of these specks were white and some were colored. The larger ones could be seen to have definite shapes, although it was not possible to see very many details of their structure. A 10-power hand lens showed much more. The tiny specks were seen to have a definite shape. One thing was sure. I had collected thousands of individual small animals and plants. All of them had lived in a few gallons of pond water.

It was the bigger animals I was interested in this time. They were of two main types. One of these I recognized as *Daphnia,* a water flea. A number of its relatives were also visible. The commonest of the other type is known as *Cyclops.* It has a single red eye in the middle of its head. I had trapped many individuals as well as a few related types.

I could continue to investigate these larger animals with the hand lens, and could learn many things about their structure and how they carry on some of their life activities. They are so active and so intensely alive. The microscope, with its greater magnifying power, offers the chance to learn much more. I collected some clear pond water without concentrating it, so the animals and plants could be kept alive at home while I studied them. A quart or two-quart container with a wide mouth so that enough air can get to the animals in the jar is a good way to keep them.

Imagine an animal complicated enough to have many body parts, yet small enough to require a microscope to see its structure in detail. Complex as it is, its body covering is transparent and reveals most of its internal make-up. Imagine an animal which swims by using its antennae, while its five pairs of jointed legs serve to kick food into its mouth and help collect oxygen, so necessary for so active an animal. These are descriptions of *Daphnia* and they are accurate. They tell us only a few of the many fascinating facts about this striking and wonderful animal. It is so common and easy to collect that we ought to learn about it in a more systematic way.

Daphnia and its relatives are most common in bodies of fresh water. They are found in ponds, lakes, swamps, ditches, streams,

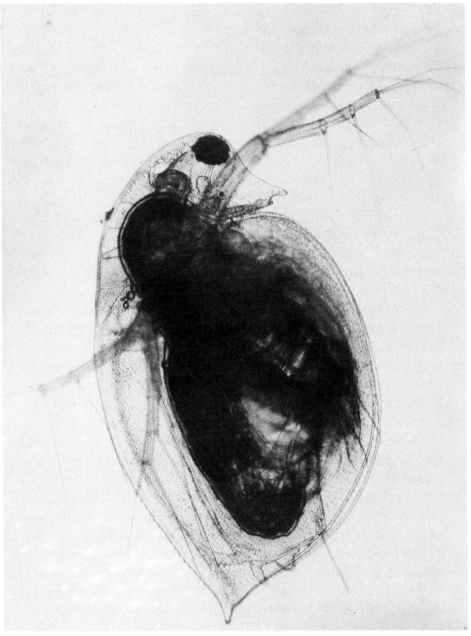

A young daphnid showing antennae, eye, an outline of the digestive tube, and the hard outer covering. In front, the two halves of the shell are shown slightly separated at the edge. The legs poke through the opening as the animal becomes active. (50 ×)

and temporary bodies of water. A smaller number are found in the salt waters of oceans and seas.

Daphnia is a crustacean—related to the lobster, the crab, the shrimp, and the crayfish. It has many other close relatives but these are the best-known ones. Crustaceans have jointed legs and a body covered by a shell made of a chemical called chitin. Chitin is a hard, tough material. How can an animal such as *Daphnia* grow when it is confined by an outer coat which is not alive? It grows because it is able to shed the chitin covering regularly by molting. Then the softer inner parts of the body grow until a new, larger chitin cover forms and hardens.

The shell is a single structure which is folded over so that it seems to be made of two halves. It is attached to the body just below the head, and the rest of the body lies free between the two halves. The two valves open in front so the lower part of the body can be pushed out between the front edges of the shell.

The head and the thorax, the next section of the body, each bear a number of pairs of jointed legs or appendages. The second pair of head appendages—the antennae—are heavy, jointed, and branched. They are quite long and move actively. The antennae, or feelers, move the animal through the water in erratic jumps. No wonder this very common creature of ponds and ditches was first called the water flea.

The next three pairs of head appendages are hard to find because they have been changed as the animal developed and have become part of the mouth structure. They are used in getting food.

Just below the mouth opening is the beginning of the thorax, the next section of the body. It bears five pairs of flattened, leaflike legs which beat to and fro in rapid motion. This does not move the animal but does set up currents of water which flow in between the halves of the shell. The water brings precious oxygen gas to the feathery legs and the surface of the body. The current flows between the legs, close to the body and upward toward the mouth opening, bringing with it particles of food. In a way *Daphnia* kicks its food into its mouth.

The rear part of the body is the abdomen, which has no legs, and is bent forward under the front part of the body. The transparent shell makes it possible to look through the animal in X-ray fashion.

Daphnia has a long digestive tube which is usually seen in outline since it is commonly packed with food. It begins at the mouth and continues to the tip of the tail at the end of the abdomen. *Daphnia* feeds on bacteria, small green plants, protozoa, and little bits of

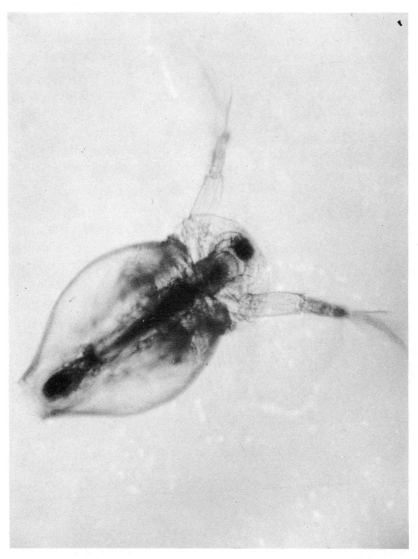

A very young daphnid seen from the back where the shell is folded. This one had recently emerged from the mother's brood pouch. The body is so thick that most of the structures are not sharply in focus. (60 ×)

decaying matter which it filters out of the streams of water that the
legs kick toward the mouth. The gut squeezes the food along. The
food is digested on this journey through the alimentary canal. What
remains undigested is expelled from the opening at the end of the
digestive system.

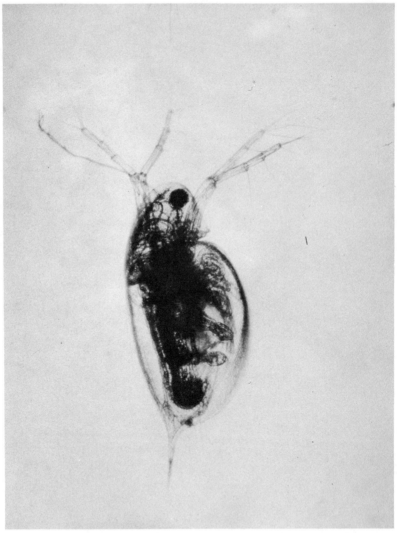

A young daphnid after the first molt. The legs are clearly visible as is
the antennae which provide the power for moving the animal. Note that
the brood pouch is empty. At this stage the animal is not ready to
produce eggs. (40 ×)

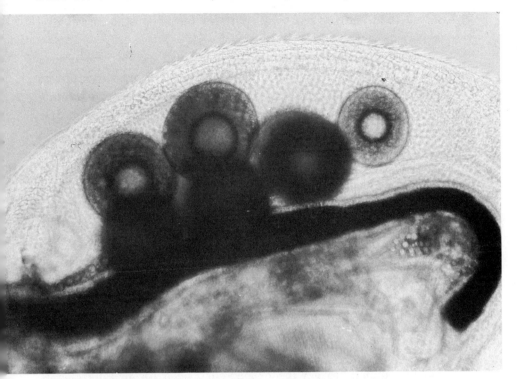

A close-up photograph of the brood pouch with six food-filled eggs before they have started to develop. Although they remain in the pouch until development is completed, all the food required is in the egg and none is provided by the parent water flea. The dark tube is the lower end of the digestive tube. (50 ×)

Daphnia has a rapidly beating heart which pumps a blood fluid throughout the body. One of the exciting sights in looking at the animal under a microscope is the rhythmic pumping of the heart—up to three hundred beats every minute. The heart is a simple sac with three openings. A pair of holes, one on each side, receives the blood after it has traveled around the body. The third opening faces forward. Each squeeze of the heart forces blood through this opening into the body spaces.

There are no blood tubes to carry blood, no veins or arteries or capillaries. It travels, instead, through the spaces of the body in a fairly regular path and bathes all internal parts of the animal. It returns to the heart to be pumped around again. The blood brings dissolved food and oxygen to all parts of the body and carries dissolved wastes away from them.

The rate at which the heart pumps is affected by the temperature of the water. When the temperature is low the heart slows down; when the temperature is raised, the beat quickens. You can see this for yourself if you have a microscope. Count the rate when you first examine the animal. Place the slide with daphnid in a refrigerator for ten or fifteen minutes and count the beat again. You should notice a sizable change.

Daphnia has the reddish, iron-containing chemical, hemoglobin, in its blood. A similar substance is found in the blood of all animals with backbones. The hemoglobin is not contained in cells (red blood cells) as it is in vertebrate animals, including man, but is dissolved in the blood fluid.

When the waters in which *Daphnia* lives are rich in oxygen, the blood is colorless. When the water is poor in oxygen, the blood is quite red in color. We do know that when these animals are producing eggs which will develop into young *Daphnia* in the mother's body, the hemoglobin is deposited in the eggs. It might help the developing animals to get the oxygen they need for making energy available for all their activities.

When a pond containing *Daphnia,* rich in hemoglobin, becomes clear again, the daphnids slowly lose their red color as the water increases its supply of dissolved oxygen. It takes about ten days for the red color to disappear.

Daphnia does have cells in its blood fluid in large numbers—the wandering white blood cells. They defend the body of the water flea against disease organisms, just as similar cells in our body attack and destroy bacteria and other disease germs in our body.

The work of white blood cells was first suspected by a scientist who was studying *Daphnia*. It happened that most of the animals he had collected were infected with a yeast parasite. He saw these invading organisms and saw the crawling white cells of the daphnid surround and destroy the yeast cells. He followed this clue and realized that the human body also had cells of this type. He called them *phagocytes,* which means "eating cells" and perfectly describes their function.

Daphnia has a very large eye right in the middle of the head. It is

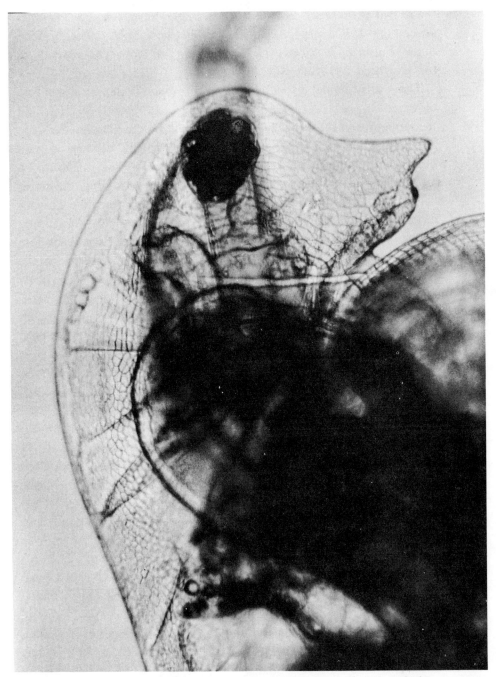

The head of the water flea with the prominent eye and three of the muscles which move it. The first section of the digestive tube is shown, as is the structure of the outer shell. (50 ×)

really two eyes which fuse to form a single one when the animal is developing. It is a strange eye, moving first here, then there, in short, quick, quivering motions which never seem to stop. The movements are produced by three pairs of muscles.

The eye is made up of a number of separate lenses—one type of water flea has twenty-two. It is a compound eye, something like the large eyes in the housefly, the dragonfly, and the grasshopper.

We think that the eye must be sensitive to light, because we can observe the animal's behavior when it reacts. *Daphnia* seems to be attracted to light, and yet, when the sun is shining brightly, the water flea moves away from the brightness. Toward evening, the animals move upward again, toward the surface and the light. Apparently *Daphnia* are influenced by the intensity of the light. It may be that factors other than light also affect the vertical movements in the pond, toward and away from the surface. But it does not seem likely that an eye such as *Daphnia's* can receive images such as we know.

There is a "brain" in the head. It is a nerve center which supplies a large nerve to the eye. It is also connected with a double nerve cord which is a center for nerves to the legs and the rest of the body.

Reproduction and development in *Daphnia* are strange processes. During most of the year, only females are to be seen. This is unusual, since so many millions upon millions of individuals are found in even a small body of water. Where do they all come from?

Each female water flea has a large ovary just behind the middle of the intestine. It produces eggs and passes them into a space between the body and the shell. This open space lies just below the heart and serves as a brood pouch. It is here that the eggs develop into young daphnids which are miniatures of the parent. The number of eggs produced varies from one or two to as many as forty or more in some individuals.

The strangest thing about reproduction in the water flea is that there are no males to be seen most of the year. The eggs develop without being fertilized by a male reproductive cell. This unusual process in which an egg develops without fertilization is called *parthenogenesis*. It happens in this way in plant lice (aphids), honey bees, and a few other animals.

Development takes from two to four days. The young are then pushed out of the brood pouch by movements of the abdomen. When

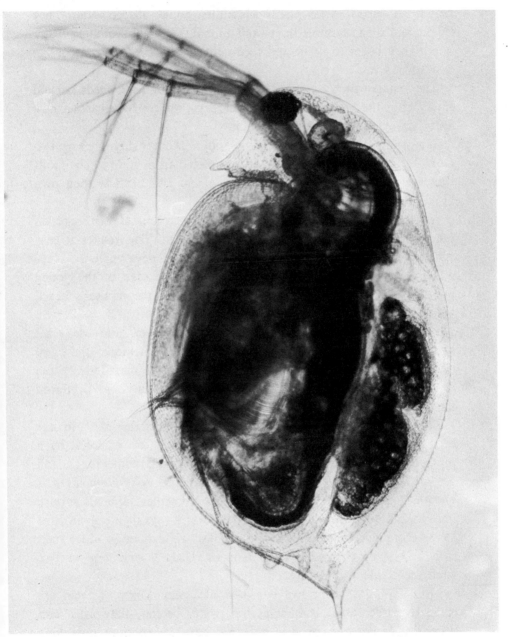

Many details of structure of *Daphnia* are visible in this photograph. Two young, far along in their development, are in the brood pouch. Just above the top one is the heart, while the feathery appendages of the legs which function in respiration are clearly seen. (50 ×)

they first escape they lie quietly while their bodies absorb water. They fill out and soon resemble the parent animal. They are miniature water fleas. They begin to swim and feed actively. By now they are living their own lives.

The female which produced the brood of young soon sheds her old shell. When the newly formed shell hardens, the ovary releases a new batch of eggs into its brood pouch.

The young daphnids grow rapidly and molt every day or every two days. When they have grown and completed from four to six molts they are mature enough to produce eggs and give birth to their own broods of young.

Any collection of *Daphnia* will include some animals with eggs in the brood pouch in some stage of development. This makes it easy for anyone to observe some of the changes in development.

Early in development a beating heart can be seen in the young animals. Its beat is not as rapid as the beat of the mother's heart, which can also be seen at the same time.

When males are found, they are few in number, and are a bit smaller than the females. They are formed from some of the eggs, often when cold weather is not far off. The males then fertilize the eggs of females which are therefore different than those produced through the rest of the year.

The fertilized eggs almost complete their development in the brood pouch. Development is suspended as they are enclosed by a protective covering. The fertilized eggs are called winter eggs, and are released with the cover into the water. The *ephippium,* as it is known, floats or sinks into the mud. The incomplete animals survive until their development is revived by the warm rays of the springtime sun. All animals which emerge are females, which soon produce their own broods of parthenogenetic females. Usually only one or two winter eggs are found in each case.

Most daphnids never live out their life span. Many of them are eaten by larger animals such as fish, water beetles, flatworms, and water bugs. Because of this it is not easy to discover how long daphnids would live in their natural environment if they were not eaten. One other threat to their lives is the parasites such as bacteria, yeasts, and molds which attack them.

It is necessary to grow *Daphnia* in the laboratory to answer any

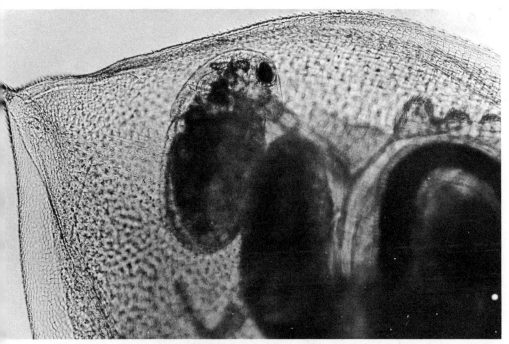

The same animal from the previous photo, one day later, with the young animals close to the completion of their development. The one on the left is easy to recognize as a daphnid. (50 ×)

questions about its life span. By providing the animals with favorable conditions it was found that daphnids live a life span of some fifteen to twenty-five molts; that is, from thirty-six to fifty days. It was also found that the life span could be extended by lowering the temperature in which they were grown. You would expect that raising the average temperature would shorten the life span. It does.

In attempting to find some explanations, one experimenter cultured two identical groups of daphnids at temperatures which were 10 degrees apart. All other conditions for the two groups were the same. The experimenter found that the animals kept at the higher temperature showed a much faster rate of heartbeat. They also lived a shorter time—a fact which was already known. Other groups of water fleas were grown at different temperatures in following up this clue. In every instance, the higher the temperature, the shorter the life span. When the number of days the average animal lived was multiplied by the number of beats per day it was found that the total

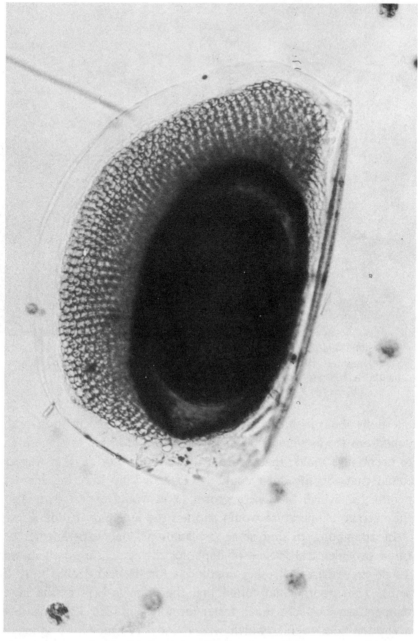

A winter egg (ephippium) of *Daphnia* with a single fertilized egg in its protective covering. After spending the winter in the mud, it develops in the early spring and emerges as a parthenogenetic female. (60 ×)

for all animals at all temperatures was very much the same. It almost seemed as though each animal had so many heartbeats. When this number of beats was expended, the animal could not remain alive any longer. It is not being suggested that the same conclusions apply to man. But the idea does have some interesting possibilities.

Daphnia is only one of several hundred species of water fleas found the world over. They are alike in many ways and their relationships are easy to see. Most of them are important as food animals for a number of varieties of fresh-water fish.

The other water fleas also bear strange names, such as *Moina, Bosmina, Polyphemus,* and *Simocephalus.* They are common in fresh waters and they do resemble *Daphnia.*

When we notice that two different animals or plants have many characteristics in common we think that they are related in some way. The characteristics we look for are basic structure, life history, and similar traits. The more closely they resemble one another, the more closely they are related. The fewer the traits they share, the less closely are they related. The scientific names given to living things and the groups to which they are assigned tend to indicate the relationship. Relationship means common ancestry—a similar heritage. Naming living things and grouping them are part of taxonomy, the science of classification.

Experts put all water fleas in a group called Cladocera. The name comes from two Greek words meaning "branched horns." This, of course, refers to the single large pair of antennae which stand out so prominently in *Daphnia* and its relatives.

Water fleas are important as food for many larger fresh-water animals. They are also collected in quantity and sold as live food for many kinds of tropical fish grown in home aquariums. Tropical fish shops often have supplies of the live animals that can be bought for as little as a quarter. For this you will be given thousands of animals— enough to keep you busy for weeks. Be sure to put the animals in many times the amount of aquarium water you receive with them.

There is an even more interesting way in which daphnids perform a valuable service. Water-supply reservoirs often serve as excellent breeding places for large populations of microscopic green plants. Many of these give our drinking water a bad taste and smell. They

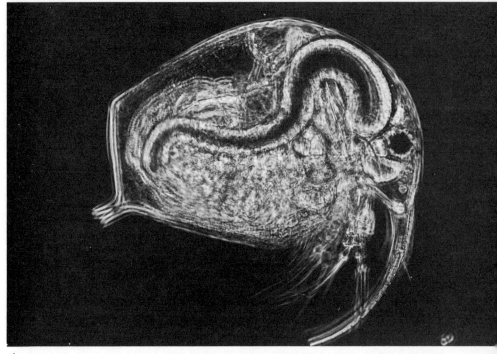

A

Three fresh-water relatives of *Daphnia*—all fairly easy to recognize as relatives.

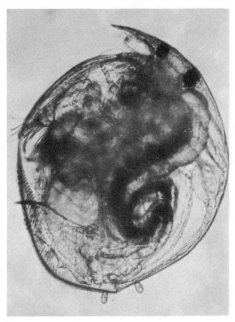

A. *Bosmina.* (55 ×)
B. *Simocephalus.* Note that the eyes here are paired. (55 ×)
C. A young *Polyphemus* just after emerging from the brood pouch. (100 ×)

B

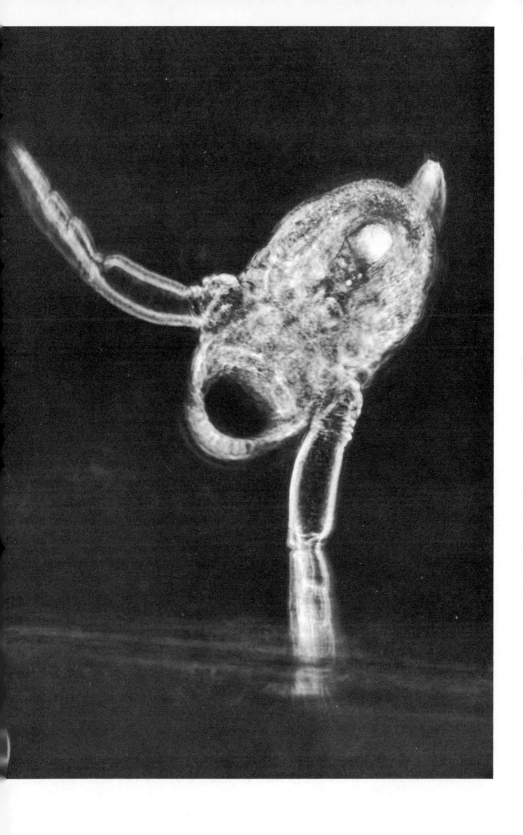

must be removed before the water can be delivered to our homes as fit to drink.

If the water-supply engineers tried to filter off the trillions upon trillions of individual plants they would need screens so fine that the openings would soon clog and little if any water would flow out of the reservoir.

So numbers of daphnids are added to the waters of a reservoir. The water fleas devour the tiny plants in tremendous amounts. They graze the waters the way cows and sheep graze the land. They flourish, with so much food, and multiply rapidly. They are so large that very coarse screening can be used to filter out the daphnids and the waters will flow through the screen with no difficulty. The collected daphnids are then scraped away from the screen as they accumulate. How many daphnids are collected in a year from such screens? The amount is measured in *tons*—even from a small reservoir. This probably represents hundreds of thousands of billions of animals—all so that we can drink pure, fresh water.

Another fascinating crustacean which is sure to be found in any collection of fresh water is the red-eyed *Cyclops*. This animal belongs to a group called the copepods, the largest group of all the crustacea in terms of numbers of animals and numbers of species. Most copepods are smaller than the water fleas but they are billions of times more numerous.

The copepods are as important in the salt waters of the earth as are the water fleas in fresh waters. They number at least five thousand different species and are so prolific that it has been suggested that the total number of individual animals of this group is greater than the total of all the other many-celled animals combined. This means more than all the individual grasshoppers, ants, bees, flies, beetles, mosquitoes, fish, frogs, birds, clams, snails, and all other types together.

If this is too hard to visualize, consider this. When a long fine net is drawn through the water and collects hundreds of thousands of small animals in a bottle, over 90 per cent of the collection will consist of copepods. Picture how many are found in stretches of thousands of miles of ocean in all directions. We can't give a sensible number as an estimation of their population at any one time; but we do know that the copepods are the main source of food for fish of all types in the sea and that even the huge whales feed on them directly or indirectly. The part they play in the web of life in salt water is a major one.

The name *copepod* means "oar-footed" and describes the legs these animals use to swim through the water. The typical copepod has a well-defined head plus a body and a tail section, or abdomen. It has no separate shell like the one covering the water flea. One fresh-water copepod looks like a longhorn steer when its long antennae are held at right angles to the body. Most copepods have specialized mouth parts and usually only four pairs of swimming feet. In many varieties, the females have one or two prominent sacs of eggs attached to the tail part of the animal.

The single eye, often red in color, is located in the center of the head. The body is transparent and the internal organs are easy to see. There is a digestive system but the animal does not have a pumping heart as do the water fleas. There is a blood fluid which is moved through the body spaces by the movements of the gut. There is also a nervous system with a nerve cord and a number of branching nerves. No special structures for the exchange of gases in respiration are evident. Oxygen is probably absorbed through the entire body surface.

Copepods feed on diatoms, bacteria, protozoa, rotifers, and other small organisms in the waters in which they live. Their life cycles are a bit different from the cycle of the water flea. With a little patience it is possible to watch the cycle and to see some details.

Copepods are most common in the sea. Many varieties are beautiful to look at. Some have hairs modified into unusual featherlike structures; some are colored brilliantly. *Calanus* is one of the marine types which has been studied in much detail. It is a major food for the herring and other important food fishes.

Cyclops is the most common of the fresh-water copepods and will appear in almost any collection of water from a fresh-water source. Its development can be observed and has been by many students.

Male and female cyclops mate as a result of chance contacts in the water. The male transfers a packet of male reproductive cells to the body of the female. The eggs are fertilized by the male cells as the eggs pass from the ovary, where they are made, into the egg sacs,

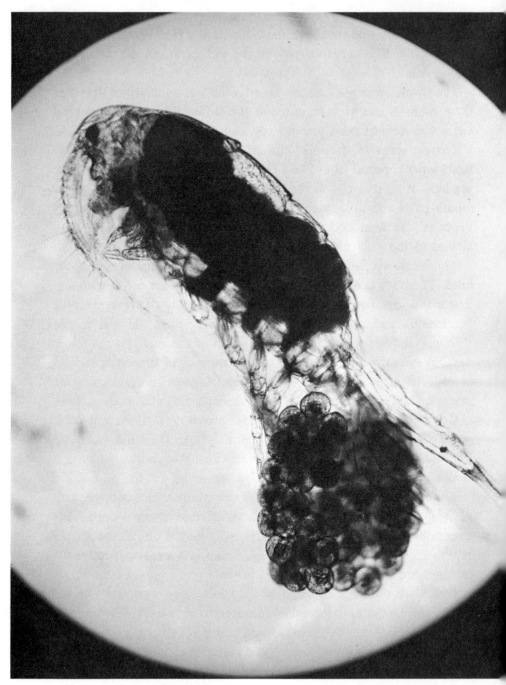

A copepod shown from the side with an egg sac containing many eggs attached to the female. (70 ×)

where development begins. Development takes from one to five days and depends on the temperature of the water and possibly on some other factors as yet undiscovered.

When development within the egg is almost complete, the eggs show a change of shape. Each of the two egg sacs contains between fifty and sixty eggs. Hatching is signaled by an appendage poking through the egg membrane. The egg bursts open and releases a small animal which looks very little like the adult which produced it. It does have three pairs of jointed legs and a single eye. It lies quietly as its body absorbs water and fills out. Then it begins to swim around actively and to feed. It has a long way to go in becoming an adult cyclops.

An immature animal that does not resemble the adult which produced it is called a *larva*. The larva of *Cyclops* with its three pairs of legs is called a *nauplius*. The three pairs of legs of the nauplius do not become the legs of the adult. Rather, they develop into the antennae and mouth parts of the mature animal.

The nauplius feeds, grows, and molts to form larger, more advanced nauplius stages. There are six molts in all. The formation of a new cyclops is not yet completed.

Most crustaceans pass through a nauplius stage in their life cycle, although in some, it is completed while the developing animal is enclosed by the egg membrane. The last of the molts of the nauplius produces still another kind of larva which begins to look like the adult. The life cycle is still not complete. Four more molts produce larger versions of the second type of larva. A final molt finally gives rise to a new adult.

This complex cycle requires from eight to as many as fifty days, depending on the conditions. Adults can live anywhere from four to nine months. An adult female will produce new pairs of egg sacs at intervals of from two to six days. In an average cyclops female lifetime some twelve pairs of egg sacs are produced. No wonder ponds, lakes, and seas are so full of copepods.

The adults and the second larval stages are able to resist drying out in mud for years by secreting a protective membrane around themselves.

As noted earlier, there are thousands of species of copepods in salt and fresh waters. It is not difficult to find many varieties in any

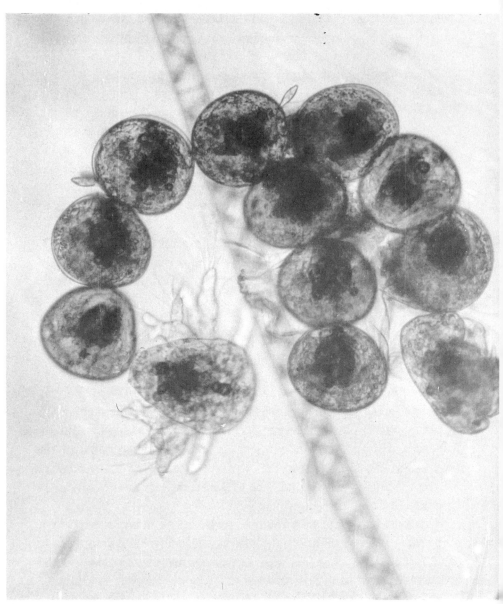

A

A. An egg mass of *Cyclops* which was detached from the female.
One nauplius larva has just emerged from an egg and others are showing
signs that they, too, will pop open. (75 ×)
B. The nauplius, after an hour, has filled out with the water it has
absorbed and now looks like a typical nauplius. (100 ×)
C. The last larval stage before the adult cyclops is formed. (100 ×)

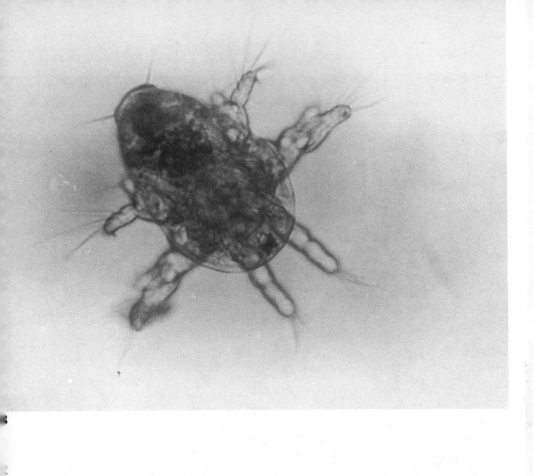
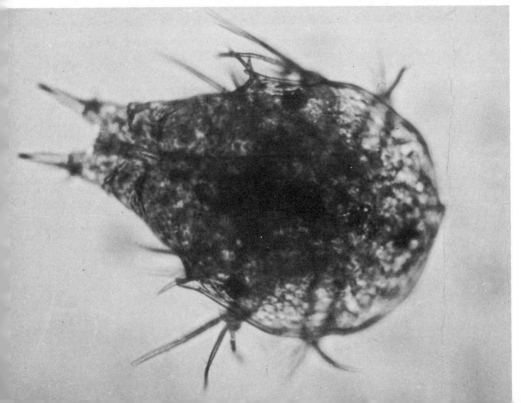

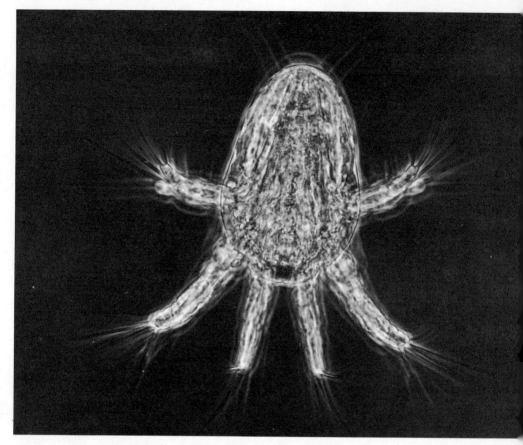

A nauplius larva of a salt-water copepod—easily recognized as a nauplius
yet looking different from the nauplius of *Cyclops*. (100 ×)

collection. If you are able to identify them, their names will again
sound strange—names such as *Diaptomus, Canthocampus, Eure-
temara,* and *Parenchaeta.*

Although the copepods are the major crustaceans of salt waters
while the cladocera are basically fresh-water animals, there are a
few kinds of cladocera—relatives of *Daphnia*—which are regular
inhabitants of the sea and are often collected in large numbers. Two
species are often seen in my plankton collections from ocean and
bay. They, too, bear living young which are miniatures of the adult—
just as in *Daphnia.*

The photographs of *Evadne* and *Podon* show how much they

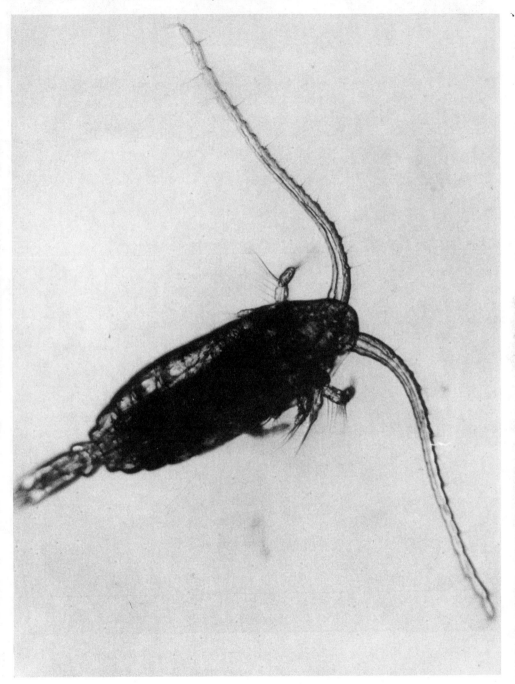

One of the most common and plentiful copepods of the ocean. It is related to *Calanus,* the most plentiful and prolific of all. (40 ×)

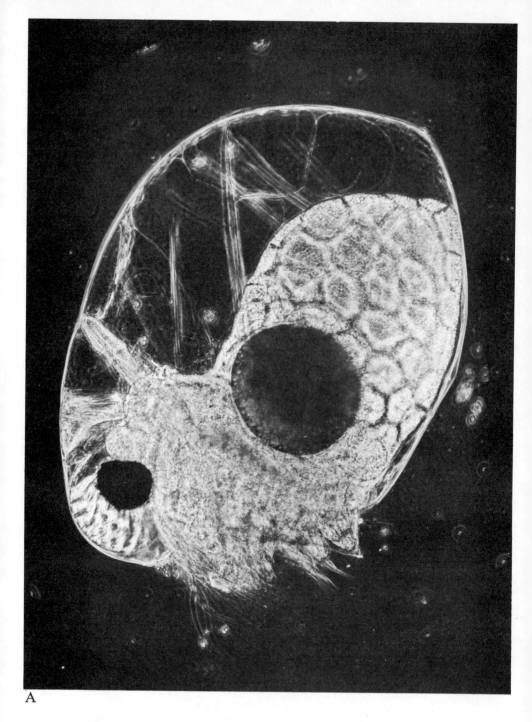

A

One of the two common cladoceran relatives of *Daphnia* from marine waters. This one is named *Evadne*.

A. The adult with no eggs visible in the brood pouch. (75 ×)

B. The same species with eggs visible before development starts. (55 ×)

C. *Evadne* with six young in the brood pouch. The unusual, large single eye is clearly shown in the adult and in two of the young. (55 ×)

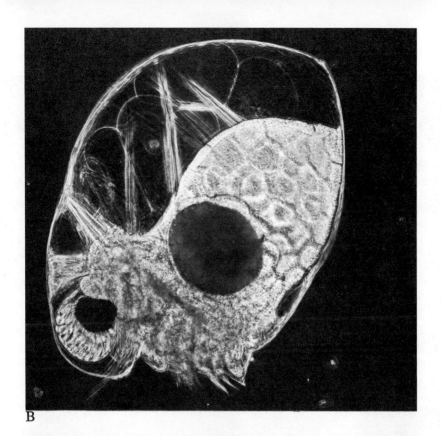

B

C

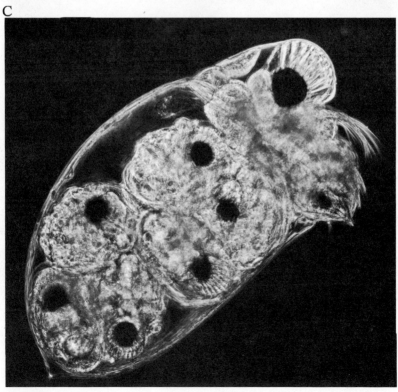

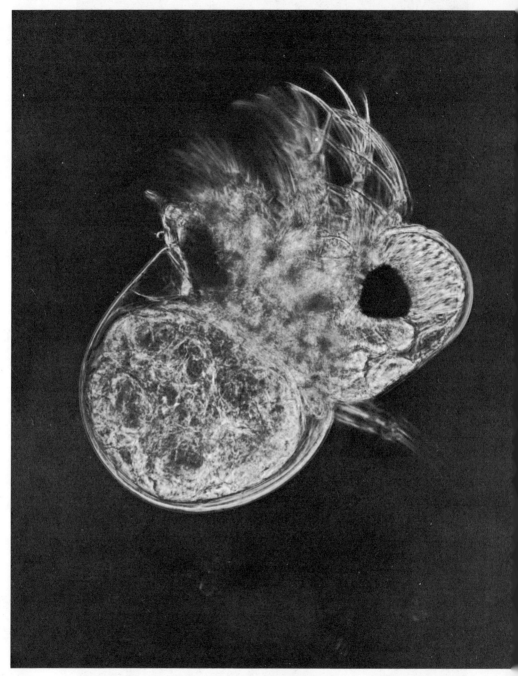

A young *Podon* after it has emerged, fully formed, from the brood pouch. This is another salt-water relative of *Daphnia* and often appears in collections in the late spring and early summer. (100 ×)

resemble *Daphnia*. Their eyes are even more prominent, even in the young in the brood pouch. They have been studied but many questions about them are still unanswered. This is true of so many organisms of the ocean. The science of oceanography is beginning to come into its own with many more scientists attracted to this rapidly growing science, but there is still a great need for individuals who are able to add to the fund of information about life in the sea.

Another interesting relative of *Daphnia* is one which also lives in fresh water. One pond which never failed to yield an interesting assortment of organisms rarely produced *Daphnia*. The pond was not without its cladoceran population. Every time I collected at this site, my collecting bottle was alive with a relative of *Daphnia* called *Polyphemus*.

Polyphemus is a lively fellow, more erratic in his movements than *Daphnia* and not as easy to draw up in a medicine dropper to put on a slide. It, too, has a large eye. The name *Cyclops* comes from Greek mythology where it is used to describe a race of one-eyed giants. The name was first given to the fresh-water copepod. When *Polyphemus* was discovered it was given the name of one of the Cyclopes.

Chapter 7

SPINNING TOPS AND OTHER LARVAE OF THE PLANKTON

The oceans and seas support the richest variety of living things on the earth. This variety includes some of the largest and most spectacular animals as well as many of the smallest whose life stories have not yet been fully studied.

I am most interested in microscopic life in all kinds of places, but especially in water. The microscopic organisms in the ocean form a community of drifting life found mostly in the upper layers.

The waters of the ocean move ceaselessly with many kinds of motion. Currents—large and small, vertical as well as horizontal, swift and slow—provide some of the forces which move it. Tidal action and waves add their bit by continually stirring it.

Many large, powerful animals have no difficulty in swimming effortlessly through the water. They often swim against the most powerful currents and make progress. Whales, sharks, fish, and other animals can swim great distances. The organisms of the plankton are not able to move with such direction. They drift, carried along by wave action and currents, to places their own energies are not able to carry them.

Whenever I drew my cone-shaped plankton net through the waters of ocean and bay, I always found in the collecting bottle a supply of plankton organisms which I could observe—and sometimes photograph. At times the bottle was yellow with the tens of thousands of individual dinoflagellates of the type called *Ceratium*. They were swept up during the time when their numbers were increasing so fast it amounted to a population explosion.

On another trip it was the large circular diatom *Coccinodiscus* whose numbers were so great that they almost clogged the fine net. The "oar-footed" copepods were always plentiful, as were worms of many types and in several stages of their development. A few water fleas, such as *Evadne* and *Podon*, will be found in each collection. These organisms are always a part of the plankton. They are the base of a kind of food pyramid—the source of food for the rest of the life in the sea.

There is another part of the plankton which will intrude in many collections and demand attention. This consists of the organisms which do not remain as plankton but move on to other careers in other parts of the ocean. The majority of them are larvae—stages in the life history of some animal so different in appearance that it is often difficult to connect them.

You are probably most familiar with larvae of animals that live— at least for a time—on land. The often colorful and frequently strange or fierce-looking wormlike caterpillars complete their development as attractive butterflies or moths which give little evidence in their appearance of their earlier life.

Beetles, flies, dragonflies, and many other kinds of insects also have life histories which include a larval stage that shows little or no resemblance to the more familiar animal which finally emerges. Tadpoles are also larvae which do not look much like the frogs or toads to which they later give rise.

The larval way of life originated long before insects or frogs appeared on the scene. The causes of their development in many groups of animals are not clear. It does seem that the development of the larva had great value for many of the types of animals in which it appeared. It is also clear that different types of larvae appeared as stages in the life history of many unrelated groups of animals—as well as in some related ones.

Marine waters almost always will yield some larvae. Fresh waters usually contain fewer types, but this is to be expected. Larvae are a part of every environment, even if only for a short time. They play a significant biological role. It is for this reason that biologists have devoted so much attention to them.

The larval stage is generally produced as an egg completes the first stage of its development. In the story of *Cyclops,* the nauplius larva is the first product of the egg. It looks nothing like the adult which produced the egg. The nauplius feeds actively and grows rapidly. Its development includes the formation of still another type of larva before the transformation to the adult takes place.

This type of life history is often the story of many marine animals. Two or even more larval types may be part of the life story of many of them. Unless it is observed as it takes place, it is often difficult to connect the larval types.

Because larvae are so much a part of the marine environment, especially of the plankton, it brings them into our drops of water and makes us want to know more about them. Many of the larger animals of the ocean are either slow-moving or even attached to some solid object throughout most of their lives. Starfishes, sea urchins, snails, segmented worms, and barnacles are a few animals of this type. Eggs and sperms of these animals are shed into the water where fertilization takes place. Millions of eggs are produced almost daily by a wide variety of animals that live in the sea.

What would happen if all the eggs produced young which then proceeded to compete with each other as well as with the parent organisms for the limited food and space available? It should be obvious that very few could survive. If a few of each type survived until they were breeding adults, they could replace those which were eaten or which perished in other ways.

Most of the adults are attached, or they move so slowly that their habitat is a small area close to where they originally settled. How are these animals able to spread and to populate areas of the ocean far from the place their eggs were laid?

Fertilized eggs are light and readily become part of the plankton. The larvae to which they give rise are also part of this community. The movement of the water carries them great distances from their starting point. In the plankton stream they find much food to sustain them. Many of them serve as food for larger animals. Others survive long enough to complete their development. These sink to the bottom or attach themselves to begin a new phase of their lives.

The slow-moving stages are often found far from the place of their beginning. Many kinds of organisms independently developed larval stages, some of them unique; others were similar to those produced by other animals.

A life history with larval stages must have survival value since it appears in so many successful types. These thoughts come to mind in finding out about and then wondering about the ways of living things—how some of them manage to survive and then to flourish.

The crustaceans are the most plentiful animals in the sea both in numbers of individuals and in numbers of species. A group of animals so successful in populating the waters would be expected to show great efficiency in reproduction. A variety of larval stages is part of the efficiency of crustaceans and no doubt contributes to their success.

Most crustaceans pass through one or more larval phases. Some of the more complex species complete several of the stages before the animal emerges from the egg. Collections of sea water generally contain some crustacean larvae.

The nauplius larva is the simplest and most common type. The body is usually oval in shape and bears three pairs of jointed limbs. There is a single eye in the middle of the head. The legs do not become legs in the adult but they develop into the antennae and some mouth structures in the fully formed animal.

The legs move so rapidly they seem to vibrate. The result is an inefficient kind of motion which seems to set the body spinning. The outer skin is hard and the nauplius grows the way adult crustaceans do—by a series of molts. There are many nauplius types but it is easy to recognize each one as a nauplius.

Another common larva is the *Cypris* larva. It resembles the adult, even though superficially, of a group of Crustacea called Ostracoda. The name of this group comes from a Greek word meaning "shell." The animal is completely enclosed within a hinged shell which opens to allow the jointed legs to poke through.

One of the barnacles passes through a nauplius and then a cypris stage before settling down and attaching itself permanently as an adult. The complete transformation is a remarkable one and to witness even a part of it is a rewarding experience. Once it has settled down to an adult existence it no longer is part of the plankton community.

Nauplius larva of a barnacle. In this stage of the barnacle's life it is a swimming animal of the plankton. (80 ×)

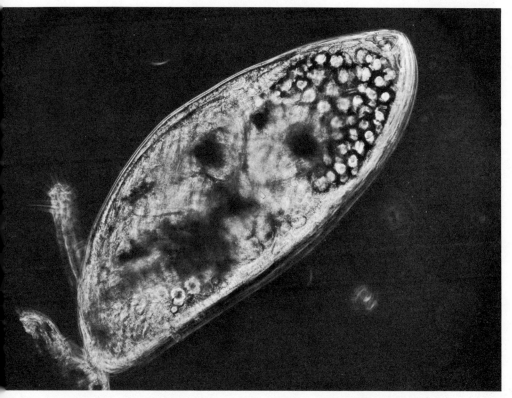

The cypris stage of the barnacle. It is still an actively moving animal, but near the end of this phase it attaches itself and remains attached for the rest of its life. In this later stage it is no longer a microscopic animal or a member of the plankton. (55 ×)

Early in the spring and continuing on into the summer, plankton collections contain many strange-looking larvae, each with a long spine projecting from the back and with a pair of huge, stalked eyes. They are *zoea* larvae and they are part of the life cycle of crabs, shrimps, and prawns.

The zoea larva is an advanced stage and shows body segments behind the structure which will become the head. The nauplius consists only of the head region. All zoea have passed through the nauplius stage and still have changes ahead before they are ready to drop to the sea bottom for development to be completed. The adults also are no longer part of the plankton.

The annelid worms are the major worms found in the ocean. They are segmented worms; that is, their bodies consist of a large number

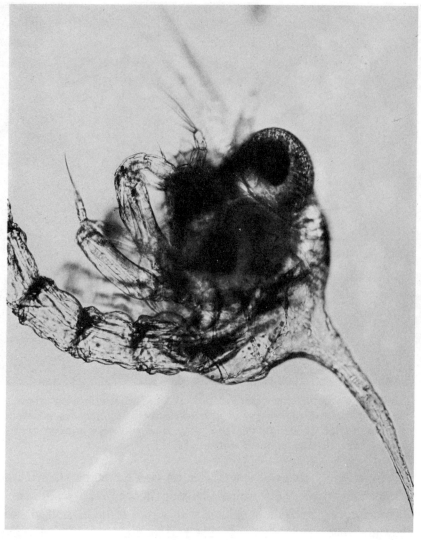

A zoea larva of a crab. Except for the large, stalked eyes, it is not easy to see the connection between this strange creature and an adult crab. (30 ×)

of sections attached end to end. They look like so many little rings attached to one another. The Latin word for ring is *annelus;* thus the name for the group. The common earthworm is an annelid but over 90 per cent of the annelid species live in salt water.

A few small adult annelids are found in the plankton. Most annelids produce larvae which spend some part of their lives as plankton organisms before they settle down as adults. Most of them live in the mud on the shallow ocean floor, often in tubes they construct.

The typical larva of the annelids is the *trochophore,* the spinning top. It spins because its structure includes a ring of cilia which beat powerfully to propel it. The most delightful description of this larva is found in the witty, but strikingly accurate verses written by Dr. Walter Garstang, a long-time student of marine life. The following lines are taken from his book *Larval Types and Other Zoological Verses.*

> The Trochophores are larval tops the Polychaetes set spinning
> With just a ciliated ring—at least in the beginning—
> They feed, and feel an urgent need to grow more like their mothers,
> So sprout some segments on behind, first one, and then the others.
> And since more weight demands more power, each segment has to bring
> Its contribution in an extra locomotor ring:
> With these the larva swims with ease, and, adding segments more
> Becomes a Polytrochula instead of Trochophore.
> Then setose bundles sprout and grow, and the sequel can't be hid:
> The larva fails to pull its weight, and sinks—an Annelid.

A look at the three photographs of a trochophore, a polytrochula, and a young annelid should help you follow the rhyme with ease. *Trocho* comes from the Greek word meaning "wheel" (or "ring"), and *phore* means "to bear." Once additional segments are added it becomes a many- (*poly*) ringed (*trocho*) larva.

Dr. Garstang's delightful verses are deceptively simple. They describe the activity and development of many types of larvae with meticulous accuracy. In some he advanced some significant theoretical explanations which traced the relationships and meaning of larval life.

Most mollusks produce a trochophore larva in their life cycle. In some cases the trochophore stage is completed in the egg. In some others, including marine snails, oysters, and other shelled bottom-dwelling animals, the trochophore passes through a transformation in which it develops two large lobes with many cilia. The new structure is a very efficient locomotor organ called the *velum.*

This larva is called a *veliger,* which means "velum bearer." *Velum*

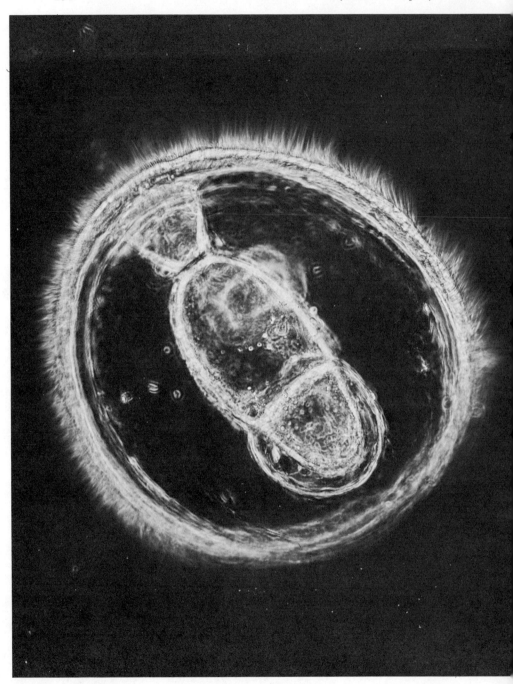

Trochophore larva of an annelid worm. The many, rapidly beating long
cilia make it easy to see why this animal's motion should be a spinning
one. (75 ×)

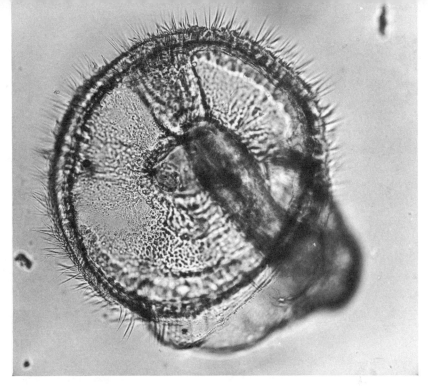

A later trochophore beginning to add rings. They are not clearly shown since they hang down and are out of focus. It is now becoming a polytrochula. Notice how clear the long cilia are. (55 ×)

A young annelid before it settles down. Notice the long bristles—the technical name is *chaetae*. This accounts for the group name, Polychaeta, which means "many bristles." (55 ×)

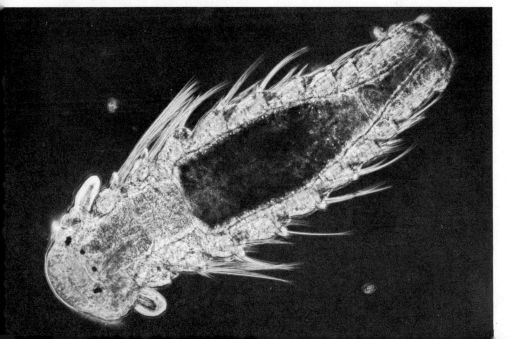

is the Latin word for "sail," which suggests something about the way this larva looked to the first microscopist to observe and name it.

> The Veliger's a lively tar, the liveliest afloat,
> A whirling wheel on either side propels his little boat;
> But when the danger signal warns his bustling submarine,
> He stops the engine, shuts the port, and drops below unseen.

This is the first of seven four-line verses which make up the entire poem. The rest of the verses develop an involved story of the remaining course of development which has much technical information. The verse quoted is so accurate and recalls for me the exasperation of trying to photograph the veliger as it sailed through my drop of water. No sooner was I ready to expose the film in the camera than

A veliger larva of a small marine snail. The ciliated velum, or sail, is nicely shown. The shell is beginning to form and can also be seen. This one did not close the port and so the photograph tells part of its story. (100 ×)

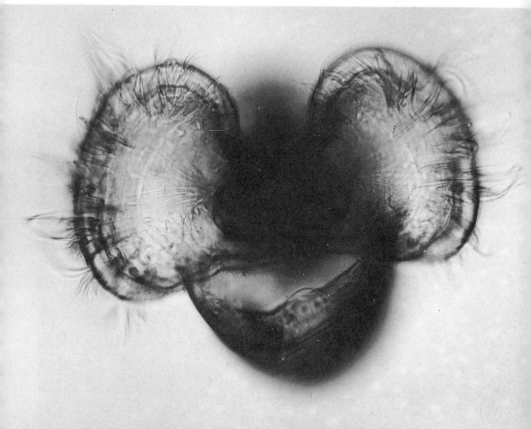

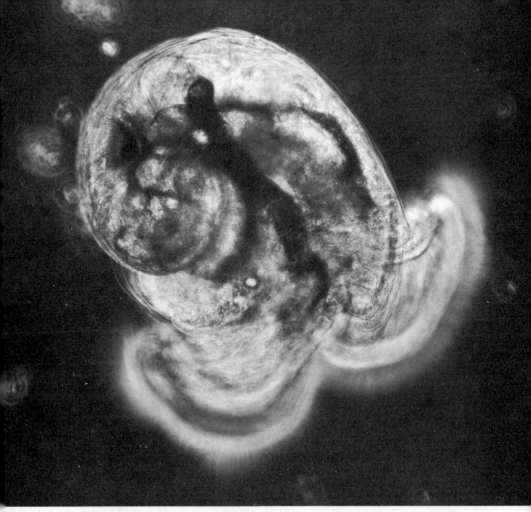

A later veliger with the coiling of the shell plainly shown. It is also possible to see some structures within the fleshy body inside the shell. (100 ×)

some object in the water touched the velum and it was withdrawn so quickly that the picture would not be the one I wanted. I succeeded only because I was determined to get a shot which showed the larva as it should be seen.

Although the veliger is equipped with a kind of sail, it is one of nature's first successful motorboats. The cilia beat strongly and push the animal along through the water. The veliger photographed is the larval stage of a common marine snail. The shell is not evident at first; later it is easy to see. The internal organs can also be seen, as well as the start of the fleshy foot which will serve as the locomotor structure of the adult snail.

By the time the shell is well formed, the velum is no longer a prominent structure. The animal is now too heavy to remain a plankton organism and it sinks to the bottom to begin its life as an adult.

The starfish and its relatives, such as the sea urchin, the brittle star, and others are all bottom-dwellers as adults. They move very slowly and look nothing like the larval stages which are part of their life story.

The larval types all have bands of cilia. These propel the tiny organisms into the plankton stream where they feed on smaller plankton as they grow and develop.

The common starfish goes through two distinctly different larval stages. The first one is called a *bipinnaria* and it shows no signs of the animal it will later become. It soon begins to change its form and

A bipinnaria larva of the common starfish. It hardly looks like the animal it will become. (100 ×)

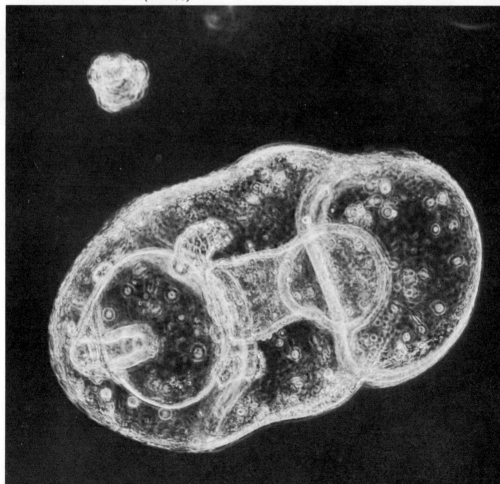

A brachiolaria larva—the next stage in the development of the starfish. The dark structure at the top is the beginning of the hard outer covering of the animal. The long, slender structures are the first of many tube feet, the unique locomotor structures of the starfish. (75 ×)

details of its structure to become a *brachiolaria*. In this stage the hard outer skeleton begins to take shape and the strange and unique tube feet of the adult starfish also can be distinguished.

There are many other larval types which may or may not show up in collections. It really depends upon how often collections are made and where and when they are made. The few additional types mentioned here are included because their first appearance was a puzzle to me. I was able to photograph them. Their identification took longer but I finally remembered seeing drawings of them in some of the books I used as references.

One of the most interesting ones was the larval stage of an animal with a distant relationship to man and all other backboned animals. Man is a vertebrate, as are all other mammals, birds, snakes, lizards, turtles, frogs, salamanders, and fishes. All these types of animals share a number of important traits. The most conspicuous of these is the backbone of vertebrae which is part of the internal skeleton.

There was a time in the long history of life on the earth when there were no animals with backbones. Many other groups of animals had succeeded in remaining alive. All of them together are sometimes called invertebrates—that is, animals without backbones. It is thought that the vertebrates developed from one or more of the advanced group of invertebrates.

One of the groups of living animals which suggests something of the connection is a strange group of marine animals called the sea squirts. The adults are small, attached organisms which look like leathery water sacs with openings through which streams of water are squirted. It is not easy to accept as an ancestor so strange an animal—even if its relationship is so remote.

The sea squirts produce larvae in which the evidences of relationship are much easier to see. They are called *tadpole* larvae for their apparent resemblance to the larval stages of frogs and toads.

The larvae are free-swimming animals of the plankton. The long tail attached to the stout body contains a supporting internal structure called the notochord. All vertebrates develop a notochord in the early stages of their life. The notochord of the vertebrates is replaced by the backbone of many vertebrae. In the sea squirts the notochord disappears when the adult replaces the larval animal.

The one pictured in the photograph is the larva of a sea squirt called *Clavelina*. When collected it was beginning to attach itself with its tail. This is a preliminary step to the change of the body to the adult stage while the tail is completely absorbed.

The plankton will often yield flatworms, sea mosses, roundworms, arrow worms, and jellyfishes which produce some type of larva. Often the collections will include adults which are as interesting as the larvae.

The world of microscopic life is a world full of surprises. Imagine an animal that swims with hairs, whose body is built like a telescope with sections that slide over one another. It can collapse suddenly and just as suddenly stretch out so it is many times its folded length.

Some of them have eyes of ruby red located deep in the neck, not near the front where we would expect to find them. Others attach themselves to objects in the water while others are covered with a glasslike armor sometimes supplied with sharp spikes or strange-looking plates.

When they are attached, a structure that looks like one or two turning wheels, or airplane propellers, brings streams of water toward the mouth and pulls along in the stream smaller animals or plants

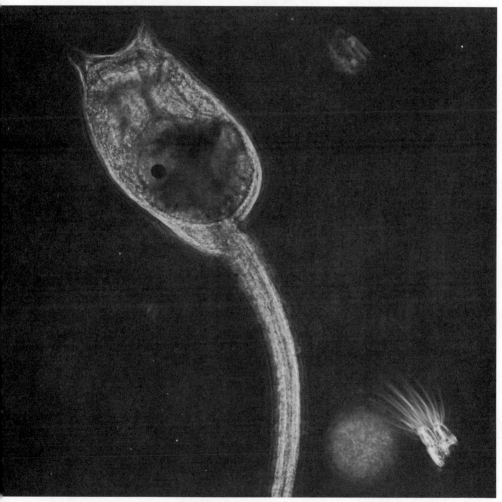

Tadpole larva of a sea squirt—*Clavelina*. The tail had already attached itself and would gradually have disappeared as the body section changed into the adult—an attached animal. The tail contains the notochord, the reminder of the association of the animal with the vertebrates. (75 ×)

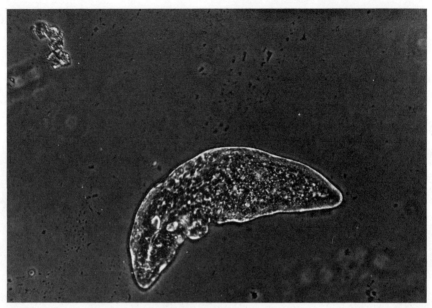

An adult, free-living flatworm of the marine plankton. It moves so rapidly that it was not easy to photograph it. (55 ×)

A young sea walnut (also called a sea gooseberry). This is a young animal, but it is not a larvae since its structure resembles the adult. Some sea walnuts are phosphorescent although there were not enough of them in the waters I searched for this effect to be noticed. (30 ×)

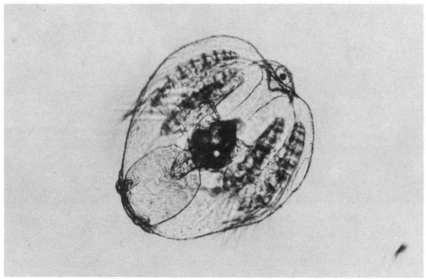

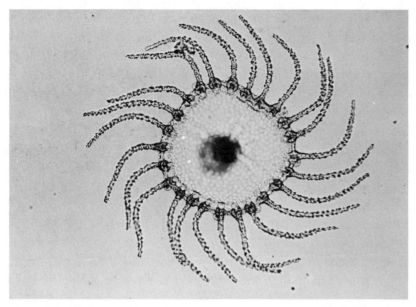

A young jellyfish with its many tentacles, each armed with batteries of stinging cells. Even bigger jellyfish than this one are part of the plankton. (30 ×)

A young prawn or lobster. It has already passed through a number of larval stages in reaching this condition. There were many in the water when I collected these; all were about the same size. (30 ×)

which serve as food for the bigger animal. Once in the body they are torn to bits by jaws located deep inside the body.

No; this is not science fiction. It is a reasonable description of a group of animals called rotifers. It is not a big group of animals, nor is it a very important group to man. But it is an exciting group to observe and a most difficult challenge for the photographer, because these animals move ceaselessly.

Rotifers are found in all kinds of fresh water all over the world. They often appear in artificial ponds and in aquariums in which there is decaying material. They also occur in salt waters as part of the plankton.

Rotifers are small. Most of them measure from 100 to 500 microns in length (from 0.1 to 0.5 millimeters). It requires a microscope to see them. Some of the smaller rotifers are smaller than large protozoa. This is true even though the protozoan consists of a single cell unit

Three different species of rotifer. The wheel organ is not shown in these. Two of them have visible eggs. Rotifers are so sensitive that they contract at the slightest disturbance. This makes them difficult to photograph.

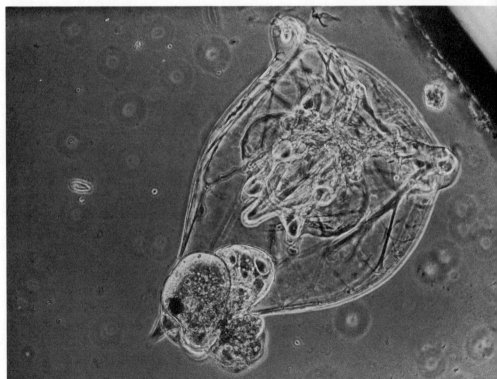

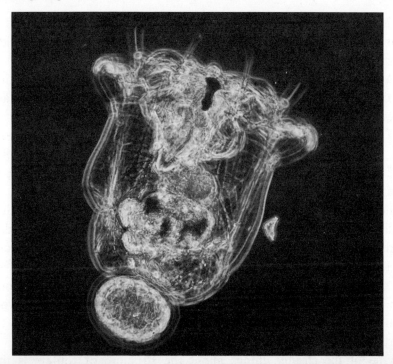

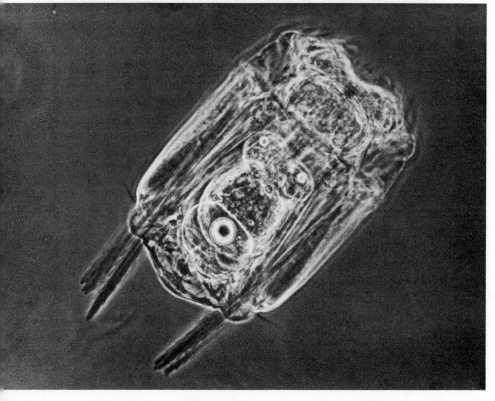

while the rotifer is composed of almost a thousand. The front end of many rotifers bears one or two circular wheels with many rapidly beating cilia.

Any collection of rotifers will contain mostly females. Once in a while a male will be seen. It is much smaller than the females and lives for a few days.

The rotifer body is enclosed in a firm but elastic covering. Inside the body are muscles whose contraction collapses it in a telescoping action. When the animal is not swimming freely, it creeps along by this telescoping motion.

Following a rotifer as it swims through the water, even as little water as makes up a drop, requires very fast reactions. They dart here, then there; they stop instantly and are off in another completely unexpected direction. It is not easy to understand such apparently random movements or their causes. They do suggest some kind of controlling structures, since the animals have a nervous structure with a flattened brain and some nerves which connect the parts of the body with the brain.

One of the strange things about the structure of rotifers is that some of them have a constant number of cells or nuclei in the bodies of all adults. In one species, for example, there are always exactly 960 nuclei.

During most of the year, the females produce young by parthenogenesis. In some types the eggs are retained in the female body until development is almost complete. In others, the eggs are released into the water where they hatch in a day or two. The unfertilized eggs generally develop into females.

When males are produced the females can form eggs which require fertilization by sperms of the male to stimulate their development.

One of the special talents of rotifers is that they can stay alive in spite of very bad conditions. If the waters of a pond dry up, the rotifer builds a thick wall around itself. It squeezes out the extra water inside the wall. In this state a rotifer can live for years even though it is as dry as dust. When rains fill the pond, the rotifer soaks up the water and begins its active life again.

Chapter 8

A FEW WORDS ABOUT CLASSIFICATION

What wonderful and exciting horizons were opened up to the early microscopists! Every day brought new discoveries. These men were studying a completely unexplored world—an amazing world of life in the waters they investigated. The tiny animals and plants crawled, rolled, floated, twisted, swam, and squirmed by their view.

Every animal and plant being seen for the first time had no name by which it would be recognized by others. If the observer wanted to add the information he had found to the body of common scientific knowledge, he had to describe the organism fully and to name it in some way. Early microscopists attached such strange and unusual names to such strange and unusual living things.

Leeuwenhoek called his "little beasties" or "little animalcules." Others used Greek myths to find names to fit the organisms they were observing. An attractive glass sponge was called Venus's-flower-basket while a rather ugly sea worm was named Aphrodite after the goddess of love and beauty. The lively little creature with a single red eye in the middle of the head was named *Cyclops* after the race of one-eyed giants whose eye is found in the middle of the forehead.

We know today that there are over a million different species of animals alive on the earth. We must add to this vast number over a quarter of a million species of living plants. New species are being discovered almost daily. What shall they be called? How do we know that a particular plant or animal has or has not been seen and named before? What do the names tell us? Why not use the common or popular name by which some organisms are known?

The answers to these questions are both practical and scientific. Men have, for a long time, been interested in the relationship of living things to one another. They were also aware that they needed to know which organisms meant danger and which were beneficial. All of these facts meant that identifications had to be accurate. It makes quite a difference that the smooth sumac or the dwarf sumac be separated from the poison sumac and that each one be readily recognized.

People the world over use popular names for plants and animals familiar to them. If we are not familiar with the language of these people, what does the name they use mean to us? How much sense can they find in the common names we use? What tree are we referring to when we call a woody plant ironwood? It really depends upon where we are when we call a plant ironwood. Over two hundred distinctly different species of woody plants are called ironwood in different parts of the world.

The first person to put some order into this chaotic situation was Carl Linné, a Swedish botanist. He had a genius for order and classification and put it to use in developing a system of naming and classification still used in its basic form by biologists today. It is known as the binomial system. This refers to the fact that every plant and animal species is identified by two names. Linnaeus, as he called himself, named and classified the plants and animals known to him about two hundred years ago.

In the Linnaean system man was called *Homo sapiens* while the sugar maple was known as *Acer saccharum*. The common house cat bears the scientific name *Felis domesticus* while the grizzly bear is known as *Ursa horribilis*. *Homo, Acer, Felis,* and *Ursa* are *genus* names. A genus is a group of living things which are closely related and which have many important traits in common. *Daphnia, Cyclops, Evadne,* and *Paramecium* are also genus names.

Some genera (plural of genus) have many species. Thus, there are silver maples, red maples, Norway maples, and sycamore maples as species of maple; but there is only one living species of man. The names *sapiens, saccharum, domesticus,* and *horribilis* are called species names. The members of the same species have even more traits in common than do those which are in the same genus.

The binomial name or scientific name of any known species of plant or animal includes the genus and species name. It does not take long to become familiar with the way in which names are used.

How can we account for the traits by which we recognize a particular plant or animal? The qualities which keep appearing in all members of a genus or species must be inherited. This helps explain why organisms in the same species or genus are related. In what other way could they acquire the same hereditary qualities?

The scheme of classification does not end with the genus. Biologists have devised larger and larger categories to group plants and animals that are still related but that have fewer and broader traits in common. The term Crustacea was used to describe the group which includes *Daphnia, Cyclops,* the lobster, the shrimp, and many other animals that have a number of characteristics in common. This group is called a *class.* There are so many thousands of species of animals in the class that it must, for convenience and meaning, be divided into smaller groups called *orders.* The order containing all the water fleas is called Cladocera while *Cyclops* belongs to the order Copepoda. Orders are made up of smaller groupings called *families* which in turn include one or more genera.

There is one bigger grouping than the class. This is the *phylum.* The Crustacea belong to phylum Arthropoda, which means "jointed legs." It means much more than this and includes other qualities in common. The group also includes other classes of animals with jointed legs—insects, spiders, centipedes, as well as other animal types. The arthropods make up the largest of all animal phyla in numbers of species included—over 750,000 living types at least.

The names are strange to you now but as you learn more about plants and animals you will see the logic of the system. New varieties of plants and animals will fit in their proper place and the oneness of the living world will be more apparent.

Enough, now, of words and pictures. The real delights of the world of microscopic life are to be found in hunting with the microscope. All that has gone before in this book was designed to be a long and enticing invitation to enter this world of endless enchantment and discovery. I hope that the study of the micro-universe will help you to understand something of the universe of larger life, the one we constantly have before us.

Appendix 1

HOW TO MAKE A MICROPOND

There are many ways to start and to maintain a supply of fresh-water microorganisms. The simplest way is to collect some fresh-water organisms from a pond, lake, swamp, or other source. It is a good idea, at the same time, to collect some additional containers of clear pond water for later use.

When you return with your collections, uncover the containers and squirt in air from a medicine dropper to stir up the water and aerate it. It is best to put your containers with their organisms in a refrigerator for storage until you use them. The organisms can be maintained for a week or more in this way.

The best containers to use for a micro-aquarium or micropond are one pint or one quart wide-mouth glass jars. The jars in which peanut butter is sold are excellent for this use. Wash the jar thoroughly with water; rinse, and allow it to dry by exposure to air.

Fill the jar to three-quarters of its height with clear pond water, spring water, or tap water. If you use tap water, allow it to stand for two or three days with no cover—exposed to the air. This will permit the dissolved gases which might harm your microbes to evaporate from the water.

One way of providing food for your microbes is to add four or five grains of uncooked rice, wheat, or some similar seeds. Cover the container loosely with its own cap or a piece of cardboard. Keep the

A micropond I set up using the instructions in Appendix 1. I used a
timothy hay infusion to prepare this
one. It is now teeming with microscopic life—mainly protozoa of a
variety of types.

container in a cool place and away from the direct light of the sun.

In a week or less, the grains will show signs of decay. They will probably be partly covered with a fuzzy mass of fine threads of mold or they will be attacked by bacteria. You can recognize bacterial decay by the cloudy look of the water close to the grains being broken down. Soon after this, the water may also begin to show the presence of some tiny protozoa which can be seen as white specks moving slowly through the water.

If you have collected pond water with its population of organisms, you can, when the seeds have begun to decay, add a drop or two of the pond water with its microbes. Even if you do not add micro-organisms to your culture, spores of bacteria and mold, along with cysts of protozoa which are light enough to be floating around in the air on particles of dust, will fall into your jar and will start multiply-ing. Food will be provided by the grains you have put in it. In turn, the bacteria, mold, and decaying grains will serve as food for the pro-tozoa.

Another excellent source of food for a micropond is hay, especially timothy hay, which you can get from a riding stable or any other place where horses are kept. Take six to ten 2-inch lengths of the stalks and boil them in a small amount of water. The resulting amber-colored fluid should be allowed to cool before adding the stalks and liquid to pond, tap, or spring water.

The hay will decay, as did the grains, and it will also support the growth of bacteria and molds. These will be followed by a succession of a variety of protozoa. If you keep a micropond for several weeks, the protozoa will be succeeded by rotifers and other larger microorganisms.

A micropond will be a rich source of microorganisms for several weeks. At that time you can set up fresh containers with water and food source and seed it with organisms from your older cultures. This can keep you supplied with organisms for some time.

Marine organisms are much more difficult to culture. The best procedure for keeping any you have collected for a week or more is to dilute the collection with clear sea water and keep it in a refrigerator when it is not being used. Many of the marine plankton organisms will survive long enough for you to observe them a number of times.

HOW THE PHOTOGRAPHS WERE MADE

Almost all of the photographs of microorganisms were made by the author. The few illustrations from other sources are acknowledged in the legends. If you are interested in some of the details of how the photographs were produced, the following information may be of some help.

Two microscopes were used in making all photographs. The first one was a Nikon SKe with its photomicrographic attachment. This includes a 35 mm camera body and a focusing telescope for locating the organisms. This camera had an assortment of bright field and phase contrast lenses along with the necessary condensers. About one-fourth of the photographs were made with this microscope.

The second camera used is the one pictured in the illustration, and is the one still being used. It is a Wild, Model M-20, a Swiss-made instrument. This is a research-type microscope which includes a complete photomicrographic attachment—two interchangeable camera bodies; one using 35 mm film, the other taking 120-size roll film and yielding $2\frac{1}{2} \times 3\frac{1}{4}$ negatives. The binocular eyepiece of the microscope is used for locating the organisms and for focusing them. This microscope has ten objective lenses—some bright field and some phase contrast—which permit magnifications from 18 $\times$ to 1500 $\times$.

Panatomix X film, a relatively slow film, was used in making all negatives. It is a very fine grain film and yields negatives of such

A stereobinocular microscope. This is the low-power microscope used to survey all collections and to select those used to prepare microscope slides for higher-power magnification and possibly for photography.

sharpness that enlargements of 11×14 and larger were easy to produce.

I developed all of the film in Microdol X developer. I made some of the enlargements reproduced in the book but most of them were produced by a custom finisher.

Over a thousand negatives were produced in the course of preparing the photographs which were finally chosen. Some of them are still not as good as I would have wanted them to be, but the photography of living things is a never-ending challenge to patience and skills. An electronic flash would have stopped the motion of some of the organisms and would have yielded sharper negatives. Since the photography

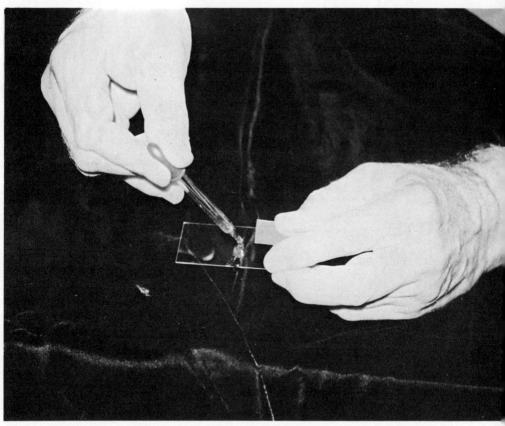

Preparing a slide for microscopic examination. The main problem is to put just enough water on the slide to fit under the cover glass and to avoid air bubbles when the cover glass is added.

of marine and fresh-water plankton is a continuing interest, an electronic flash device will be tested and used in later work.

My collections were poured into shallow glass dishes called finger bowls. To make sure that the organisms keep well they were carried in wide-mouth thermos flasks. The dishes were then carefully inspected with a Nikon stereobinocular microscope—a low-power microscope which magnifies organisms from 10 × to about 30 ×. This magnification is enough to pick out and identify individual organisms for closer inspection with high-power microscopes.

Individual organisms were picked up with very fine pipettes while they were in view under the low-power microscope. The organisms so isolated were placed on a clean 3-inch by 1-inch glass microscope slide. A few organisms were added along with a drop or two of water. The drop was carefully covered with a thin cover glass.

The slide was then examined with the photomicroscope, usually at 100 × magnification. A number of exposures of each organism or group of organisms were made at magnifications of 30 × to 400 ×.

The complete photomicrographic camera and microscope being used. This illustration is included only to give you some idea of its appearance. Far less pretentious equipment has been used to produce excellent photographs.

The exposure is determined in part by trial and error, and depends on a number of factors, including illumination, magnification, kind of film used, etc. Since the animals are generally moving quite rapidly, an exposure fast enough to stop the motion is also needed. The ways in which this can be determined is considered in the book on photomicrography listed in the Bibliography.

Most of the exposures used varied from one-half second to one-tenth of a second. A careful record of every exposure was kept, along with other data such as the date, source of organisms, tentative identification, lenses used, and anything else that should not be trusted to memory alone. This then becomes an accurate source of information.

Equipment such as that described here is not essential to making good photomicrographs. There are simpler ways of producing acceptable and even good ones with small microscopes and a light-tight box as a camera. The photograph made with one of Leeuwenhoek's original microscopes should convince you.

BIBLIOGRAPHY

You may want to explore some aspects of the world of microscopic life in greater breadth or depth. There are many books available and in print. Schools and local public libraries will have some of them. Others are inexpensive and worth acquiring if you intend to follow some avenue of more intensive investigation. The recommendation of each book will be accompanied by a brief statement of its contents as well as its possible use.

A. Learning More about the Microscope and Its Use

1. DOBELL, CLIFFORD. *Antony van Leeuwenhoek and His "Little Animals."* Dover Publications. New York. 1960. If you want to know more about Leeuwenhoek and his work with the microscope, this excellent work in a paperback edition is for you. Dobell translated many of Leeuwenhoek's letters and includes much new information about his life, his methods of work, and the significance of his discoveries in the light of present information.

2. EASTMAN KODAK CO. *Photography through the Microscope.* 3rd ed. Rochester. 1962. Sound, accurate, and useful description of the methods of taking good photographs with your microscope. A little technical, but worth the effort.

3. HARTLEY, W. G. *How to Use a Microscope.* The Natural History Press. Garden City, N.Y. 1964. An excellent paperback on the theory of the microscope and a practical account of how to use it well. Not al-

ways easy to follow but worth extending yourself. This also includes some information on photography.

4. JACKER, CORINNE. *Window on the Unknown.* Scribner's. New York. 1966. A good elementary and recent introduction to the history of the microscope. Many individuals are associated with the development of the microscope.

5. SHEPHERD, WALTER. *How to Use a Microscope.* Signet Science Library. New York. 1966. Another paperback worth owning. A simpler introduction to the skillful use of the microscope than Hartley. It includes, in addition, instructions on slide making, as well as brief accounts of a variety of objects and organisms which can be studied with the microscope.

6. WELLS, A. L. *The Microscope Made Easy.* Frederick Warne. New York. In addition to a lucid, helpful account of methods of using a microscope effectively, this work includes instructions for collecting organisms and simple descriptions of the most common ones likely to be collected.

B. *Learning More about the Organisms*

1. BUCHSBAUM, R., and MILNE, L. J. *The Lower Animals: Living Invertebrates of the World.* Doubleday. Garden City, N.Y. 1960. Accurate descriptions of the main groups of invertebrates with brief accounts of key species. Magnificently illustrated with exceptional photographs in color and in black and white by outstanding photographers. A beautiful book worth browsing through from time to time. Expensive, but many libraries will have copies.

2. CURTIS, HELENA. *The Marvelous Animals: An Introduction to the Protozoa.* The Natural History Press. Garden City, N.Y. 1968. A fine introduction to the "little animalcules"; well-written and excellently illustrated. Not a guide to identification but a good source of modern information about the protozoa as organisms and about the lives of many important species.

3. CLEGG, JOHN. *The Observer's Book of Pond Life.* 2nd ed. Frederick Warne. New York. 1967. An excellent guide to fresh-water microorganisms with a large number (many hundreds) of fine color drawings. Although written about organisms found in English ponds and streams, the same genera and often species are also found in American waters. Inexpensive and worth owning.

4. HARDY, A. C. *The Open Sea, Its Natural History: The World of Plankton.* Houghton Mifflin. Boston. 1956. The *one book* to have always

at your side. Hardy is one of the world's leading oceanographers and a major contributor to its modern development. He writes with charm, wit, and great imagination about the work to which he has devoted a long, productive life. Magnificently illustrated with many water-color drawings by Hardy himself as well as photomicrographs by the master, Douglas P. Wilson.

ABOUT THE AUTHOR

George I. Schwartz, the author of LIFE IN A DROP OF WATER, is an expert on the wonderful world of microscopic life. For more than thirty-five years he has investigated fresh-water ponds and lakes and the Atlantic Ocean—making collections, studying specimens, and taking both stills and movies of what he has found. He has been a guest of countless network television programs, has prepared instructional films for school classrooms, and has been the author or coauthor of four biology textbooks.

Mr. Schwartz has degrees from New York University, and has done further work at Columbia and Adelphi Universities. After a lifetime of scientific investigations and teaching, he is now a full-time writer and lives in Princeton, New Jersey.

INDEX